THE
REALITY TELEVISION
QUIZ BOOK

THE
REALITY TELEVISION
QUIZ BOOK

Compiled by Chris Cowlin

Foreword by Christopher Biggins

;HING LTD

First published in hardback in 2010 by

Apex Publishing Ltd

PO Box 7086, Clacton on Sea, Essex, CO15 5WN, England

www.apexpublishing.co.uk

Copyright © 2010 by Chris Cowlin
The author has asserted his moral rights

British Library Cataloguing-in-Publication Data
A catalogue record for this book
is available from the British Library

ISBN: 1-906358-72-9   978-1-906358-72-3

Typeset in 10.5pt Chianti Bdlt Win95BT

Cover Design: Siobhan Smith

Printed and bound in Great Britain by
MPG Book Group in the UK

Dedication:
To my wife Julia - who watches a lot of reality TV!

FOREWORD

I was delighted to learn that Chris Cowlin was compiling this quiz book which, in an age when our fascination with reality TV continues to grow, is long over due and highly topical.

Having spent more winters than I care to remember on stage appearing in panto, it was wonderful to be given an opportunity to hang up my Dame costume for a season in 2007 to take part in the huge success that has been ITV1's I'm a Celebrity Get Me Out of Here. It was an extraordinary experience and I loved every minute of it and it was a great honour to triumph over such worthy competitors as supermodel Janice Dickinson and popstar Jason 'J' Brown to be crowned King of the Jungle.

My first taste of reality television gave me the appetite for more and I went on to appear in, amongst others, Channel 4's Celebrity Come Dine With Me. It proved to be an exhausting few days but good fun and the food was certainly a lot better than it was in the jungle! Reality TV makes compelling entertainment, it has given us some great characters and produced many memorable viewing moments and I am proud to be able to say that I have been a part of it.

The Reality Television Quiz Book includes all of the classic shows the genre has produced, from the early programmes through to the current day (I didn't know that there were so many still to appear on!) and is testament to the growing numbers of us insane enough to live out a part of our lives on TV for the amusement of others. Oh, the things we're prepared to do for fame and fortune!

Chris Cowlin is to be congratulated on putting together an entertaining and informative book which is sure to appeal to anyone who can't resist watching reality TV – I guarantee that you won't be able to put it down!

Best wishes
Christopher Biggins

INTRODUCTION

I would first of all like to thank Christopher Biggins for writing the foreword to this book. I have been a great fan of Biggins for many years.

I would also like to thank all the newspapers, magazines and famous names who have backed this book and provided a few comments (these can be found at the back of the book).

I have compiled over 40 books and I must say this has been a real pleasure to put together. There is something in this book for everyone, regardless of age, and if you have enjoyed watching programmes such as Big Brother, Blind Date, The Apprentice or The X Factor.

I decided to compile this book as reality television really has taken over our TV screens in the last ten years, and it seems people cannot get enough of it. This is the first ever quiz book compiled based on reality television so I hope you enjoy reading through the pages and testing your knowledge of some entertaining television and fame hungry contestants.

In closing, I would like to thank all my friends and family, especially my wife Julia, for encouraging me to complete this book.

Chris Cowlin.

Best wishes
Chris Cowlin

www.apexpublishing.co.uk

BIG BROTHER – SERIES 1

1. In which year did this show start – 1999, 2000 or 2001?

2. What was the first prize for series one?

3. How many housemates entered the house on the first day?

4. Following on from the previous question, can you name six of the housemates?

5. How many days did the first series last – 54 days, 64 days or 74 days?

6. True or false: The housemates failed their first task?

7. Which Irish office manager finished the show's runner-up?

8. True or false: Winner Craig Phillips actually received more nominations throughout the show than any other housemate?

9. With what percentage of the votes did Craig Phillips win the first Big Brother – 41%, 51% or 61%?

10. Which contestant was known as Nasty Nick?

I'M A CELEBRITY GET ME OUT OF HERE – SERIES 1

11. In which year was the first series broadcast?

12. Which duo presented this series?

13. Which well known DJ won this series, becoming the first ever winner of the show?

14. How many contestants were there during the first series?

15. Who finished runner-up?

16. Can you name the six star hotel the celebrities stayed at when they left the jungle?

17. Can you name the comedienne who finished fifth in the series?

18. Which Irish female presenter presented the behind the scenes show I'm a Celebrity... Get Me out of Here! Now?

19. Who was the first celebrity to leave the jungle?

20. On which television channel was the first series broad cast – ITV, Channel 4 or Sky One?

BRITAIN'S GOT TALENT – SERIES 3

21.   Which Scottish singer finished runner-up?

22.   Following on from the previous question, where did the Scottish sensation check into a day after the show final due to exhaustion?

23.   Which two months in 2009 was this show aired on ITV?

24.   Which duo presented this show in 2009?

25.   Which dance act won this competition?

26.   Which judge lasted six days before they went back to the format of three judges?

27.   What was the name of the sister show presented by Stephen Mulhern?

28.   Which musical instrument did third placed Julian Smith play?

29.   With what percentage of the votes did the winners win the final – 24.9%, 29.9% or 34.9%?

30.   Can you name the young singer who broke down in tears in the last semi-final and got the chance to sing again?

JADE GOODY

31. In which series was Jade a contestant of Big Brother – second, third or fourth?

32. Following on from the previous question, what was Jade's job before entering the Big Brother house?

33. What were Jade's middle names?

34. Who did Jade marry on 22 February 2009?

35. In which year did Jade appear as a contestant in Big Boss, the Indian version of Big Brother?

36. Can you name the fragrance that Jade released?

37. Jade attempted to run the London marathon in 2006, but which charity was she supporting and raising money for?

38. Can you name Jade's two children?

39. In which year was Jade born in London?

40. True or false: Jade was a contestant on Celebrity Big Brother 5 during 2007?

THE APPRENTICE – 2009

41. Was this the third, fourth or fifth series of this reality television show?

42. Who created this reality television show?

43. True or false: The show was broadcast on BBC One?

44. Can you name Alan Sugar's two advisors who oversee the tasks and report back to him?

45. Who won The Apprentice 2009, beating second placed Kate Walsh?

46. How many contestants were there during this series?

47. Following on from the previous question, can you name six contestants from this series?

48. At the start of each show, who is appointed to lead the teams?

49. What is the winner's salary when they are employed by Alan Sugar?

50. What is Alan Sugar's famous catchphrase when someone is eliminated from the competition?

MATCH UP THE YEAR

Match up the event to the year it happened

51.	Holiday Showdown was first broadcast	1948
52.	The only series of Farmer Wants a Wife was broadcast	2005
53.	Blind Date was first broadcast	2001
54.	The Osbournes was first broadcast	2003
55.	Hogan Knows Best was first broadcast	2001
56.	Temptation Island was first broadcast	2003
57.	America's Next Top Model was first broadcast	2001
58.	Candid Camera was first broadcast	2007
59.	Survivor was first broadcast	2002
60.	The second series of Trinny & Susannah Undress... was broadcast	1985

WHICH CHANNEL?

Match up the reality television show with the channel on which it was broadcast

61.	Wife Swap	FOX
62.	Top Chef	ABC
63.	Average Joe	MTV
64.	Fat March	MTV
65.	Pop Idol	MTV
66.	The Osbournes	Channel 4
67.	American Idol	NBC
68.	The Restaurant	ITV
69.	The Hills	Bravo
70.	Road Rules	NBC

BRIAN DOWLING

71. True or false: Brian's middle names are Patrick Robert?

72. Can you name the Irish reality television show that Brian participated in during August 2008?

73. What star sign is Brian – Gemini, Leo or Virgo?

74. What is Brian's nickname?

75. What version of Big Brother did Brian win – Big Brother 1, Big Brother 2 or Big Brother 3?

76. In which reality show was Brian a contestant during 2007?

77. Which character did Brian play in the pantomime Peter Pan at the Tivoli Theatre, Dublin during December 2008 and January 2009?

78. True or false: Brian had a short role in a new spinoff drama from Footballers' Wives during 2005?

79. Can you name the company that Brian worked for as a flight attendant before he entered the Big Brother house in 2001?

80. In which year was Brian born in Ireland – 1977, 1978 or 1979?

THE X FACTOR – 2004

81. True or false: This was the first series of this reality television show?

82. Who won the show?

83. Following on from the previous question, can you name the song that winner released, going to number one in the UK charts?

84. Can you name the group that finished as the show's runners-up?

85. Which judge was in charge of the groups?

86. Can you name the three contestants that were in the 16 to 24 category mentored by Sharon Osbourne?

87. Which female presenter presented this show?

88. Who was the winning mentor, looking after the 25 and overs?

89. Which evening was this reality television show broadcast – Friday, Saturday or Sunday?

90. Can you name the oldest finalist, aged 50, in the 25 and overs' category?

HELL'S KITCHEN – 2004

91. Who created this show and was the celebrity chef during the first series in 2004?

92. On which channel was this series broadcast?

93. Which young actress and model was the winner of this show in 2004?

94. Following on from the previous question, which team was she originally on – the red team or the blue team?

95. Which journalist had to quit the show after just one day due to injury?

96. What was the name of the follow-up programme which was made afterwards?

97. Which sitcom actor finished runner-up?

98. True or false: The UK version started before the American version of this show?

99. Who presented the show in 2004?

100. Which former MP reached the final four?

DARIUS

101. What star sign is Darius?

102. Darius's mother is Scottish but what nationality is his father?

103. What is Darius's surname?

104. At what number in the charts did Darius's self-penned song 'Colourblind' enter the UK charts?

105. True or false: Darius's first album went platinum?

106. Following on from the previous question, what is the name of the album?

107. In which year did Darius release a song titled 'Live Twice'?

108. In 2009, in which BBC show did Darius make a guest-starring role, as Italian newspaper editor, Genarro Fazio?

109. On which reality TV show did Darius find fame in 2001?

110. Up to 2009, how many top ten UK singles had Darius released – five, six or seven?

BIG BROTHER – SERIES 2

111. Which Irish housemate won the show?

112. Can you name five of the ten housemates that entered the house on day one?

113. What was the housemates' task in the first week?

114. What job did Helen Adams do before entering the Big Brother house?

115. Which English teacher from London was the first to be evicted?

116. True or false: The last task in the house was for housemates to make papier mache models of each other?

117. Can you name the contestant that entered the house on day 16?

118. Which 24-year-old contestant supported Chelsea and was a warehouse operative?

119. How many days did this series last – 60 days, 64 days or 68 days?

120. Which housemate finished in third place?

I'M A CELEBRITY GET ME OUT OF HERE – SERIES 2

121.   Which ex-England cricketer won the show?

122.   Which TV weather forecaster was the first to leave the show?

123.   In which year was this show made and broadcast?

124.   Which Changing Rooms designer finished third during this series?

125.   How many contestants were there in this series?

126.   Who was the only male actor in the Celebrity jungle?

127.   Where did ex-footballer John Fashanu finish during this series – second, fifth or seventh?

128.   Which celebrity chef was a contestant during this series?

129.   Can you name the two months during the year that this show was broadcast on ITV?

130.   Which 1980s' pop star finished in sixth place?

THE APPRENTICE – 2005

131. True or false: This was the first series of The Apprentice?

132. Who won the show?

133. How many contestants were there during this series?

134. The teams in the first week were formed by gender, what did they call their teams?

135. Can you recall the name of the property developer?

136. What was the first task during this series?

137. True or false: The reward for the winners in the third week was having dinner with Sir Alan Sugar at an Italian restaurant?

138. Who was the show's runner-up?

139. What were the apprentice teams doing at Tottenham Hotspur's ground White Hart Lane at a match against Manchester United in week nine?

140. Can you name the four contestants that got through to the semi-finals and were interviewed by Sir Alan's advisers?

THE X FACTOR – 2005

141.   Who won the show in December 2005?

142.   Can you name three of the four finalists that were in the over 25s' category?

143.   What was the name of the song the winner released after the show?

144.   True or false: Louis Walsh was one of the judges this series?

145.   Who presented the show on ITV1?

146.   Which Elton John song did Journey South sing during the first live show?

147.   Maria Lawson finished eighth in the show during 2005, what was the name of her autobiography she released in 2008?

148.   How many live shows were there, including the final – 9, 10 or 11?

149.   Who was Simon Cowell in charge of – 16 to 24s, over 25s or the groups?

150.   Who finished as the show's runner-up?

HELL'S KITCHEN – 2005

151. Can you name the two celebrity chefs who took control in the kitchens?

152. What was the prize fund for the winner?

153. True or false: This series the contestants were members of the public rather than celebrities?

154. Who presented the show in 2005?

155. In 2005, was this – series 1, series 2 or series 3?

156. Can you name three members of the red team?

157. True or false: Marco Pierre White appeared in this 2005 show?

158. On which channel was this show shown in 2005 – ITV, Channel 4 or Channel 5?

159. Who won the show in 2005?

160. Can you name three members of the blue team?

CELEBRITY WIFE SWAP

161. Who did magician Paul Daniels and his wife Debbie McGee swap with during their time on this show?

162. Which 1980s' pop singer swapped to spend time with ex-footballer Neil Ruddock in his home?

163. Which racing pundit did Edwina Currie stay with during their time on the show?

164. True or false: David Van Day appeared on this show during 2008?

165. Who is actor Bruce Jones's wife, who spent time with pop singer Sinitta's husband Andy?

166. Who was Jade Goody's partner when they went on the show?

167. Following on from the previous question, who did they swap with?

168. Can you name Samantha Fox's partner's who appeared on the show?

169. True or false: Samantha Fox spent time at Freddie Starr's home when she was on this show?

170. Which couple did singer Alexander O'Neal and his wife Cynthia swap with when they were on the show?

LEONA LEWIS

171. What is Leona's middle name – Louise, Lorna or Leila?

172. True or false: In November 2008 Leona set a record in the UK for the fastest selling download-only release with her cover of the Snow Patrol song 'Run' which sold over 69,000 in two days?

173. Which song did Leona sing during her 2006 audition for The X Factor?

174. What was the name of the book Leona released in October 2009?

175. True or false: Leona released an album in November 2009 called 'Echo'?

176. In which year was Leona born – 1983, 1984 or 1985?

177. What was the title of Leona's debut album?

178. True or false: Leona has been a vegetarian since the age of 12?

179. Can you name the title of Leona's 2007 song which was number one in the UK charts?

180. Where is Leona from – Leeds, London or Luton?

KATIE AND PETER

181. In which year was Katie Price born – 1977, 1978 or 1979?

182. Which Girls Aloud star was a bridesmaid at Katie and Peter's wedding?

183. Which TV show did Katie host in 2005 during its first series?

184. True or false: Katie and Peter took part in the 2009 London Marathon?

185. What was Katie's glamour model name?

186. What is Peter's middle name?

187. On which reality TV show did the couple meet in 2004?

188. In 2007, which award was presented to Kate by Grattan?

189. Can you name the title of Peter's song that he re-released in 2004 and went to number one in the charts?

190. In which year did the couple split up ending their three and a half year marriage?

POP IDOL – SERIES 1

191.   Who created this show?

192.   Can you name the two females who reached the last five of the competition?

193.   Who won the show?

194.   Who finished the show's runner-up?

195.   In which year was this show first shown on television?

196.   True or false: Anthony McPartlin and Declan Donnelly presented this show?

197.   What was the name of the sister show shown on ITV2?

198.   Which day in the week was this show broadcast on television?

199.   Which singer was promoted to the live shows when Rik Waller dropped out of the show?

200.   True or false: The winner was announced during February 2002?

MICHELLE McMANUS

201. True or false: Michelle won the reality show Pop Idol in 2003?

202. Which ITV chat show did Michelle appear on in 2005 – Loose Women, Parkinson or The Alan Titchmarsh Show?

203. In which year was Michelle born in Glasgow – 1979, 1980 or 1981?

204. Can you name the song that Michelle sang during the 'Elton John Themed Week', with this performance putting her in the bottom three?

205. Can you name the single that Michelle released in 2007?

206. What job did Michelle do before winning Pop Idol?

207. When Michelle won Pop Idol, she won with an excess of how many votes – 4.5 million, 5.5 million or 6.5 million?

208. What was the name of Michelle's debut album, released in 2004?

209. Which Donna Summer song did Michelle sing during the Pop Idol final?

210. True or false: Throughout the finals of Pop Idol, Michelle was only in the bottom three once?

BIG BROTHER – SERIES 3

211. Can you name the three months during the year that this series was broadcast?

212. Can you name the two contestants who walked out, one after seven days and the other after 20 days?

213. How many contestants walked in the Big Brother house on day one?

214. On which day was PJ evited – day 49, day 50 or day 51?

215. What job did Lee do before he entered the Big Brother house?

216. Where is Jonny's hometown?

217. Why were Kate and Alison reprimanded on day nine?

218. Can you recall what happened in the house in week three?

219. True or false: Jade came third in the series?

220. Can you name the two contestants from this series who got married after the show?

I'M A CELEBRITY GET ME OUT OF HERE – SERIES 3

221. Which ex-Atomic Kitten singer and TV Presenter won the show?

222. In which year was this show broadcast – 2003, 2004 or 2005?

223. Which former Spurs, Liverpool and England footballer was the fourth celebrity to leave the jungle?

224. Can you name the aristocrat who finished in fourth place?

225. Which former footballer was Alex Best married to?

226. Can you name the athlete who participated in the show, being the second celebrity to leave the jungle?

227. Jennie Bond finished as the show's runner-up, for which channel was she the former royal correspondent – BBC, ITV or Channel 4?

228. How many celebrity contestants entered the jungle during this series – 10, 14 or 18?

229. Which celebrity finished in third place - Peter André, Katie Price or Alex Best?

230. Can you name the radio DJ who was the first celebrity to leave the jungle?

THE APPRENTICE – 2006

231. On which channel was this series broadcast – BBC1, BBC2 or ITV?

232. Can you name the 34-year-old lawyer who was a contestant?

233. What was the task in the first week?

234. Who got hired by Sir Alan?

235. Can you name the 27-year-old sales manager who finished as the show's runner-up?

236. True or false: The two teams sold second-hand cars for a commission in week six?

237. Was this the second series, third series or fourth series of this reality TV show?

238. Who got fired by Sir Alan Sugar in week eight for being too 'nice' and not aggressive enough?

239. True or false: Each candidate got to be a project manager on at least one occasion?

240. Can you name the four semi-finalists that faced the interview process by Sir Alan's associates?

THE X FACTOR – 2006

241. In which month during 2006 was this show shown on ITV?

242. Who presented the show?

243. Who was the winner's (Leona Lewis) mentor during the live shows?

244. Can you name the former Brookside actor who finished the show's runner-up?

245. Who was in charge of the groups?

246. Can you name the two bands that appeared as guests on the final show, 16 December 2006?

247. Can you name the four individuals that made up the band Eton Road?

248. Which song did winner Leona Lewis sing and release when the show was finished?

249. Who made a guest appearance as a guest judge at the London auditions?

250. Can you name the four contestants who Sharon Osbourne was in charge of in the over 25s' category?

CELEBRITY BIG BROTHER – SERIES 1

251. Which charity did the show support in the first series?

252. How many celebrities entered the Celebrity Big Brother House?

253. Which comedian won the first series of Celebrity Big Brother?

254. Can you name the two celebrities who were the first to be up for eviction?

255. Which Boyzone singer finished in third place in the series?

256. Which journalist and broadcaster showed signs of stress in the house by scrawling on the dining table with chalk provided for a task?

257. In which month of 2001 was this series made and broadcast?

258. Can you name the former Brookside actress who was a contestant on the show?

259. Which professional boxer was the first celebrity to be evicted?

260. How many days did this show last – six, seven or eight?

RACHEL RICE

261.   In which year was Rachel born – 1983, 1984 or 1985?

262.   In which gothic horror film did Rachel appear along side Hugh Grant when she was eight-years-old?

263.   Which series of Big Brother did Rachel win?

264.   Which contestant finished runner-up to Rachel in the Big Brother house?

265.   On which TV show did Rachel appear during January 2009 wearing the coat of cash?

266.   True or false: In 2004, Rachel won the Wales on Sunday newspaper's Welsh Idol competition?

267.   Can you name the two housemates that Rachel voted for eviction in week 12, the last vote in the house?

268.   Can you name the two housemates that Rachel voted for eviction in week two, the first vote in the house?

269.   How many nominations did Rachel receive while in the Big Brother house – 21, 25 or 29?

270.   True or false: Rachel has a degree in English and Drama, and is a fully qualified teacher?

CELEBRITY BIG BROTHER – SERIES 7

271. Can you name the former footballer and actor who was a contestant during this series?

272. Who were the first two housemates to be evicted on day 13?

273. Which celebrity entered the house on day 6?

274. During the launch night of the show, Big Brother gave housemates five minutes to do what, winning themselves two bottles of champagne?

275. Can you name 7 of the 11 housemates that entered the house on the launch night?

276. This series was the longest ever celebrity series of Big Brother in the UK, how many days did it run for – 25 days, 26 days or 27 days?

277. When entering the Big Brother house, what was Nicola T's occupation?

278. On day 25 who entered the house in a chicken costume, pretending to be Nicola, who had just been evicted from the Big Brother house?

279. Who finished the shows runner-up?

280. Which housemate won the show?

WILL YOUNG

281. What is Will's middle name – Robert, Russell or Rodney?

282. Which reality TV show did Will win in 2002?

283. Following on from the previous question, which Jackson song did Will sing in his first audition?

284. What is the name of Will's album he released in 2008?

285. In which year did Will's song Leave Right Now reach the number one spot in the UK charts?

286. With which legendry singer did Will sing the song 'Daniel' on 31 December 2008 at the Live New Year show at the O2 Arena in London?

287. True or false: Will's first single was a double A-side featuring Westlife's song 'Evergreen' and 'Anything Is Possible'?

288. Following on from the previous question, how many copies of Will's first single were sold in its first week – 300,000, 600,000 or over one million?

289. Which X Factor judge did Will help, giving his opinion on the boy contestants during 2009?

290. In which year was Will born – 1978, 1979 or 1980?

SHAYNE WARD

291. What is Shayne's middle name?

292. In which year did Shayne win The X Factor?

293. Which football team does Shayne support?

294. True or false: In 2002 Shayne reached the final 30 of Popstars: The Rivals, the television show that was won by Girls Aloud?

295. What was the name of Shayne's first single?

296. True or false: Shayne's first single was a UK number one?

297. Can you name the title of Shayne's second album, released in 2007 reaching number two in the album charts?

298. In which year was Shayne born – 1983, 1984 or 1985?

299. Which X Factor judge was Shayne's mentor during the live shows?

300. What was the name of the single that Shayne released in 2007, the best position in the UK charts being number six?

SURVIVOR – SERIES 1

301. Can you name the 24-year-old detective constable who won the first series?

302. On which TV channel was this reality show broadcast?

303. In which year did this reality TV show first hit television screens?

304. What was the grand prize - £10,000, £100,000 or £1 million?

305. How many contestants were there in the first series?

306. True or false: The contestants were free to discuss and scheme about who they wished to vote off?

307. Where in the world was the island, this was also the site of the first American Survivor series?

308. Can you name the initial two tribes?

309. How many people watched the first series of this reality TV show – 4.4 million, 5.5 million or 6.6 million?

310. Can you name the runner-up, who lost 7-0 in the jury vote in the final?

I'M A CELEBRITY GET ME OUT OF HERE – SERIES 4

311. In which year was this series shown on television?

312. Which Bristol born model appeared on the show, finishing in fifth place?

313. Which comedian won the fourth series?

314. Which former East 17 singer arrived on day two and left on day seven?

315. Can you name the contestant who did the bushtucker trial 'Hell Holes'?

316. In which two months during the year was this show broadcast?

317. How many stars did Natalie Appleton win on the bushtucker trial 'Canopy Calamity'?

318. Who was the first celebrity to be evicted?

319. How many contestants participated during this series?

320. Who finished third in this series?

THE APPRENTICE – 2007

321. Who won this year's show?

322. Following on from the previous question, how old was he when he won the show?

323. Can you name the 36-year-old Pharmaceutical Sales Manager who was a contestant on the show?

324. During the first task, the teams had to sell what in Islington, London?

325. Can you name the first person who got fired, during the first week?

326. How many times was this year's winner the project manager?

327. In which location did the teams try to sell their manufactured sweets?

328. Which names did the teams come up with in week one?

329. In which month during 2007 was the final shown on television?

330. Can you name the 27-year-old Marketing and Design Consultant who was a contestant on this year's show?

SIR ALAN SUGAR

331. What is Sir Alan's middle name?

332. Which company did Sir Alan sell in 2007?

333. For which football team was Sir Alan the chairman from 1991 to 2001?

334. What was Sir Alan's nickname as a young boy?

335. Which EastEnders actress is Sir Alan's niece (through marriage)?

336. Why was Sir Alan knighted in 2000?

337. In which year did Sir Alan fire the first contestant in The Apprentice?

338. What is Sir Alan's wife's Christian name?

339. Where in the UK was Sir Alan born?

340. Which company did Sir Alan start in 1968?

REBECCA LOOS

341. In which country was Rebecca born in 1977?

342. In which reality television show was Rebecca a finalist during 2004?

343. True or false: Rebecca was a contestant on Celebrity X Factor during 2006?

344. With whom did Rebecca spark a relationship during her time on Celebrity Love Island in 2005?

345. In 2006, Rebecca ran the London marathon and raised over £7,000 for which charity?

346. Rebecca released a single in 2008, what was it called?

347. In which year were stories published in national papers about Rebecca's alleged affair with footballer David Beckham?

348. On which show was Rebecca a guest hostess during 2008?

349. True or false: Rebecca came third on the Spanish version of the TV show, Survivor, during 2007?

350. Can you name the Sky 1 TV Drama Series that Rebecca appeared in, playing character Naomi Wyatt during 2004 and 2005?

LEON JACKSON

351. In which year was Leon born in Whitburn – 1986, 1987 or 1988?

352. With which clothing retailer was Leon a sales assistant before he won The X Factor?

353. True or false: Leon got his black belt in karate at the age of 10?

354. Who was Leon's mentor on The X Factor?

355. With which pop princess did Leon perform in The X Factor final singing 'Better the Devil You Know'?

356. In which year did Leon win The X Factor?

357. What was Leon's X Factor victory described as by the bookmakers?

358. What was the name of Leon's single, released in February 2009, but did not reach the United Kingdom official chart, as it was only available via digital download?

359. With which Canadian performer did Leon perform at Wembley Arena during December 2007 singing the song 'Home'?

360. What was the name of Leon's first single, going straight in at number one in the UK charts?

BIG BROTHER – SERIES 4

361. Which housemate was the first to be evicted?

362. Who won Big Brother, series 4 during July 2003?

363. Who finished the show's runner-up?

364. Can you name the contestant who was a chef from London?

365. Which housemate appeared on Blockbusters in 1991?

366. What was the prize during series 4?

367. True or false: There were no nominations in the final week?

368. Can you name the two housemates who were evicted on double eviction night in week 4?

369. What job did Lisa do before entering the Big Brother house in 2003?

370. How many nominations did Tania receive during her time in the house – 6, 16 or 26?

THE X FACTOR – 2007

371.   Who won the show?

372.   True or false: The 2007 show was the fourth series of this show?

373.   Who took over from Kate Thornton to present the show for the first time?

374.   How many 'yes' votes did the auditionees need to get through to the next round of the show?

375.   Can you name the fifth judge, who judged at the London auditions?

376.   True or false: This series was Sharon Osbourne's final series as an X Factor judge?

377.   Which category did Simon Cowell mentor this year?

378.   Which pop star was Sharon Osbourne's adviser, giving her opinion about the girls at Sharon's home?

379.   Can you name the single the winner sang and released after winning the show?

380.   Which male solo artist finished as the show's runner-up?

SOPHIE ANDERTON

381.   Where in the UK was Sophie born in 1977?

382.   In which year was Sophie a model for La Senza's Christmas collection?

383.   True or false: Sophie was a guest on Friday Night with Jonathan Ross during September 2006?

384.   Which British teen comedy film did Sophie appear in during 2007?

385.   On which TV show did Sophie appear following her attempts to quit smoking cigarettes during 2005?

386.   In which year did Sophie take part in the reality TV show Love Island?

387.   Following on from the previous question, what did the presenters Fearne Cotton and Patrick Kielty refer to her as?

388.   Which game show did Sophie appear on during 2009?

389.   On which show was Sophie a contestant during its fourth series on ITV during 2004?

390.   Following on from the previous question, which singer did Sophie have a disagreement with?

CELEBRITY BIG BROTHER – SERIES 2

391. Which Take That star won the show?

392. In which year was this show made and broadcast?

393. How many celebrities participated in the show?

394. Which DJ and actor was the first celebrity to be evicted from the house?

395. Which former glamour model and TV presenter finished third in Celebrity Big Brother?

396. Can you name one of the four charities that proceeds from viewer voting went to?

397. Which phone company sponsored this show?

398. Who received the most nominations, a total of six during her time on the show?

399. Which TV presenter was evicted on day seven, being the second celebrity to leave the show?

400. How many days did this show last – 10, 20 or 30?

GARETH GATES

401. In which year was Gareth born in Bradford – 1984, 1985 or 1986?

402. Which reality TV show was Gareth runner-up in 2002?

403. Can you name Gareth's wife, whom he married in July 2008?

404. True or false: Gareth took part in the 2009 Cosmo Everyman campaign to raise awareness of prostate and testicular cancer?

405. Can you name Gareth's partner when he took part in ITV's Dancing on Ice during 2008?

406. When Gareth finished as runner-up in the reality TV show during 2002 which judge signed him to the BMG label to give him a record deal?

407. True or false: Gareth's song Sunshine was a UK number one in the charts?

408. What was the name of Gareth's first single, a cover, which entered the UK charts at number one?

409. True or false: Gareth played Prince Charming in the pantomime Cinderella at New Wimbledon Theatre, from December 2008 to January 2009?

410. What is Gareth's middle name?

CELEBRITY LOVE ISLAND/ LOVE ISLAND

411. In which year did Jayne Middlemiss and Fran Cosgrave win the first series of Celebrity Love Island?

412. Which girl band was Liz McClarnon a member of when she appeared on Celebrity Love Island?

413. Who was David Beckham's former PA that was a contestant in the first series?

414. Who was the former Manchester United and England footballer who appeared in the first series?

415. In which country was the island based?

416. Can you name the title of the theme tune to the first series?

417. Which contestant in the second series was a former member of the girl group Eternal?

418. What was the prize for the winners - £5,000, £15,000 or £50,000?

419. Can you name the couple that won the second series?

420. True or false: After making this show for the second time (renaming it Love Island) ITV revealed that a third series would not be made and that it was axing Love Island?

I'M A CELEBRITY GET ME OUT OF HERE – SERIES 5

421.   How many days did this show last – 18, 21 or 24?

422.   Which former Emmerdale actress finished the show's runner-up?

423.   How many celebrities took part in the show – 12, 14 or 16?

424.   Which former Neighbours actress, who played character Annalise Hartman, was a contestant during series 5?

425.   True or false: TV presenter and antiques expert David Dickinson was a contestant during series 5?

426.   Which 'Blue' singer finished in sixth place out of the 12 contestants?

427.   Can you name the two celebrities who took part in five bushtucker trials, more than anyone else in camp?

428.   Which 'Osmond' was a contestant during series 5?

429.   In which year was the show made and broadcast?

430.   Who won the show?

THE OSBOURNES

431. True or false: This reality TV show was first broadcast
      in 2002 and last broadcast in 2005?

432. Can you name Ozzy's and Sharon's daughter who
      refused to participate in the show?

433. What was the name of the theme song for the show,
      which is a cover of one of Ozzy's songs?

434. During May 2009 Ozzy confirmed in an interview on
      BBC Radio 2 that he can no longer watch the episodes
      of this reality TV show, for what reason?

435. Who is older – Kelly or Jack?

436. Where in America do The Osbournes live?

437. Who directed this reality TV series?

438. What is Ozzy's real name?

439. What was the name of Jack's bulldog?

440. What is Melinda's occupation?

BIG BROTHER – SERIES 5

441.   How many housemates entered the house on day one?

442.   Who won series 5?

443.   Can you name the self-proclaimed anarchist, human and animal rights activist who entered the house on day one and was ejected from the house a week later?

444.   Which housemate referred to Stuart as 'Chicken Stu'?

445.   Where in the UK was housemate Victor from?

446.   Which two housemates moved to the Big Brother bedsit on day 15?

447.   Which housemate was evicted on day 50?

448.   Who was the show's runner-up?

449.   Who entered the house on day 31 replacing Emma on the show?

450.   In which year was the show made and broadcast?

CHANTELLE HOUGHTON

451. In which year was Chantelle born – 1981, 1982 or 1983?

452. True or false: Chantelle had originally applied to be in Big Brother 6 and was a stand-by for that series but was never called up, however producers decided to use her for the upcoming celebrity version of the show?

453. What was the name of Chantelle's autobiography, published in 2006?

454. Which reality TV show did Chantelle take part in during 2007 where she had to learn 'the knowledge'?

455. What is Chantelle's middle name – Violet, Vivien or Victoria?

456. True or false: Chantelle once worked as a Paris Hilton lookalike?

457. With how many GCSE's did Chantelle leave school when she was 15-years-old?

458. In which year did Chantelle win Celebrity Big Brother, as a non-celebrity?

459. How long did Chantelle's marriage to Preston last – 10 weeks, 10 months or one year?

460. True or false: Chantelle appeared in the BBC TV Drama Hotel Babylon as the girlfriend of Chris Moyles?

ANT AND DEC

461. What are Ant and Decs' surnames?

462. The duo rose to fame on which children's television show?

463. Following on from the previous question, can you name their characters, also being their names when they started their pop careers?

464. Who is older – Ant or Dec?

465. True or false: Ant and Dec presented Pop Idol?

466. Which football team do the duo support?

467. What is the title of the duo's autobiography, released in September 2009?

468. Which show did Ant and Dec start presenting in June 2007?

469. Which TV show did Ant and Dec present which was first shown in July 2006?

470. True or false: Ant and Dec once auditioned on American Idol to surprise Simon Cowell on their show Saturday Night Takeaway?

POP IDOL – SERIES 2

471. Who won series 2?

472. Following on from the previous question, can you name the title of the winner's song?

473. In which year was this show made and broadcast – 2001, 2003 or 2005?

474. Which TV channel broadcast this show – BBC2, ITV or Channel 4?

475. What was the song theme in week seven?

476. This show was a competition for singers of which age - 16–26, 16-30 or 16-60?

477. Which two television presenters presented this show?

478. Who came third in series 2, later going into children's television presenting?

479. Can you name the four judges on the show?

480. Who was the show's runner-up?

AMERICAN IDOL

481. What was this show called during its first series?

482. In which year did this show debut on the Fox network?

483. Who was the first winner of this show?

484. True or false: Sharon Osbourne was a judge on the show during 2006?

485. Which former Popstars' judge directed the audition shows on American Idol from 2002 to 2008?

486. Can you name the creator of this show?

487. Who won the show in 2006?

488. Which English TV channel broadcasts this show in the UK?

489. Can you name the judge that started the show in 2002 and left in 2009?

490. Who won the show in 2009?

HOGAN KNOWS BEST

491.   What are the names of Hulk's son and daughter?

492.   Following on from the previous question, what nickname does Hulk give to his daughter?

493.   How many series were made of this reality TV show?

494.   What is Hulk Hogan's real name?

495.   What was the name of the spin-off of this show, broadcast in 2008?

496.   Who is Hulk's longtime friend and former wrestler, who quite often comes to stay with the family?

497.   Hulk Hogan is a former what?

498.   Can you name the energy drink that Hulk endorses during the filming of the show?

499.   In which year did this reality TV show first hit American TV screens?

500.   True or false: During November 2007, it was announced that Linda had filed for divorce from Hulk after 24 years of marriage?

GIRLS ALOUD

501.   Can you name all five members of the band?

502.   In which year was the band formed?

503.   What was the name of the single for which Girls Aloud won the 2009 Brit Award for 'Best British Single'?

504.   What did the Guinness World Records list Girls Aloud as in the 2007 edition?

505.   True or false: Girls Aloud had 15 consecutive top tens from 'Sound of the Underground' in 2002 through to 'Walk This Way' in 2007.

506.   Who presented Popstars: The Rivals, the show the five band members won?

507.   Following on from the previous question, can you name the boy band who were runners-up on the show?

508.   What was the title of Girls Aloud's first single?

509.   Can you name two of the three singles that Girls Aloud released in 2008?

510.   What was the name of the band's third studio album released in December 2005?

CANDID CAMERA

511. In which year did this show initially begin on radio as *Candid Microphone*?

512. Following on from the previous question, who created and produced the show?

513. Who presented the show between 1992 and 2004?

514. True or false: A British version of Candid Camera began in 1960 and ran for seven years, the show was presented by Bob Monkhouse?

515. How many series of this show were made in the USA – 28, 38 or 48?

516. In which year was this show made into a television programme, from radio – 1946, 1948 or 1950?

517. True or false: Candid Camera produced over ten tapes of adult-oriented stunts and hidden camera gags called Candid Candid Camera for HBO and Playboy?

518. What was the tagline to this show?

519. Who presented the show between 1974 and 1979?

520. True or false: This show was filmed using single-camera set-up?

THE CELEBRITY APPRENTINCE

521.   Who did the celebrities raise money for in the first UK version of this show, aired in March 2007?

522.   Following on from the previous question, who won the show – the women's team or the men's team?

523.   True or false: In the first Celebrity Apprentice series the winning team raised nearly £775,000 for charity?

524.   Which charity did the celebrities help out during the 2008 show?

525.   Following on from the previous question, can you name three of the five celebrity females who took part in the show?

526.   Who was fired by Sir Alan Sugar in the 2008 Celebrity Apprentice?

527.   Which actor resigned during the first day of filming in 2007?

528.   True or false: Jade Goody appeared as a contestant in the women's team during 2008?

529.   Which TV and radio presenter was part of the boys' team in 2009?

530.   Which comedian was fired in the 2009 show?

COACH TRIP

531. Who was the coach driver in the first series?

532. Who was the tour guide?

533. Where in the UK did the coach trip start in the 2009 series?

534. True or false: The first series was made in 2004 and was shown on television during 2005?

535. Can you name the mother and son who won the first series?

536. How many days overall was the coach trip in the first series?

537. Can you name the married couple who won the second series, joining the coach trip on day 15?

538. Andy Love narrated the first two series, but who narrated the third series?

539. Where in Germany did the coach visit with its contestants on day eight of the third series?

540. Which couple from Sheffield were the first to be voted off in series three, on only the second day?

CHRISTOPHER BIGGINS

541. In which year was Christopher born – 1947, 1948 or 1949?

542. What was Christopher's nickname when he appeared in the TV sitcom Porridge?

543. Which Australian actress was Christopher married to between 1971 and 1974?

544. In 2008, with which former Birds of a Feather actress did Christopher briefly co-presented a Sunday morning radio show on BBC London?

545. True or false: Christopher was the winner on Celebrity Come Dine with Me, shown during February 2009?

546. Which sitcom did Christopher appear in during the 1970s, appearing once in 1973 and then again in 1978?

547. In 2009 Christopher played himself as a pantomime director in which BBC Two sitcom?

548. What is Christopher's nickname?

549. During December 2006 Christopher formed a civil partnership with which British Airways worker?

550. True or false: Christopher attended the wedding of Joan Collins and Percy Gibson?

I'M A CELEBRITY GET ME OUT OF HERE – SERIES 6

551.   Who was the king of the jungle?

552.   Which television and radio presenter was the first celebrity to leave the jungle on day 11?

553.   True or false: David Gest was a contestant during series six?

554.   In which year was this series made and broadcast on ITV?

555.   Which former Emmerdale actress entered the jungle on day six?

556.   How many stars did Scott Henshall win on his bush tucker trial, Jungle Boogie?

557.   Which television presenter and newsreader was the first celebrity to do a bushtucker trial on the opening day of the show?

558.   True or false: Faith Brown didn't do any bushtucker trials during this series?

559.   Apart from the winner, can you name the other two celebrities who stayed the full 19 days, finishing second and third?

560.   Which former EastEnders actor entered the jungle on day five?

GEORGE GALLOWAY

561. Which series of Celebrity Big Brother did George appear – third series, fourth series or fifth series?

562. In which position did George finish in Celebrity Big Brother, out of the 11 contestants – seventh, eighth or ninth?

563. What is the name of George's autobiography, published in 2004?

564. In which year was George first elected to Parliament for the City of Glasgow in Scotland?

565. In which Scottish city was George born?

566. True or false: George was the youngest ever elected chairman of the Labour party in Scotland at the age of 26, having become a full-time party organiser three years earlier?

567. When George was evicted from the Celebrity Big Brother house in 2006, which two other people were nominated for eviction?

568. During George's time on Celebrity Big Brother, what was his chosen charity?

569. In 2004, George created which political party?

570. Following on from the previous question, in 2005 George became their first MP, but for which constituency?

BIG BROTHER – SERIES 6

571. How many housemates were there during this series – 16, 18 or 20?

572. Who won this year's show?

573. What was Craig Coates' occupation before he entered the house in 2005?

574. Can you name the housemate who was Miss Northern Ireland runner-up in 1999 and was Belfast's Woman of the Year in 2005?

575. Why were Maxwell and Anthony banned from nominating during week five?

576. Who was the show's runner-up, beating Makosi to second place?

577. Who presented 'Big Brother's Big Mouth'?

578. On which day was The Secret Garden first used – day 19, day 29 or 39?

579. Following on from the previous question, can you name the three housemates who secretly entered the house on this day?

580. Who was the fifth evictee from the house, leaving on 1 July with 71% of the public vote?

I'M A CELEBRITY GET ME OUT OF HERE – SERIES 7

581. On which day did winner Christopher Biggins enter the jungle?

582. During which month in 2007 was this reality TV show broadcast?

583. Which former model finished the show's runner-up?

584. Can you recall what the camps were called?

585. Which former footballer was a contestant during this series?

586. What was the name of the first bushtucker trial?

587. Which former Apprentice star entered the jungle on day two?

588. Can you name the former manager of the Sex Pistols, who pulled out of the show a few days before the show started?

589. Of which band was Jason 'J' Brown a former member?

590. Can you name the former Hollyoaks actress who left on day 18 during the series?

BRITAIN'S GOT TALENT – SERIES 1

591.   In which year was the first series made and broadcast?

592.   Can you name the opera singer who won the show?

593.   Who was the show's runner-up?

594.   Who were the three judges during the first series?

595.   How many people watched the final performances of the show during the month of June – 10 million, 11 million or 12 million?

596.   Which runner-up was nicknamed The Monkey Man?

597.   True or false: Paul O'Grady was originally going to present the show before Ant and Dec stepped in?

598.   Can you name all six acts that appeared in the final of the show?

599.   On which channel was this reality TV show first broadcast – BBC1, ITV or Channel 4?

600.   What was the name of the winner's album he released the month after winning this show?

RHONA CAMERON

601. In which year was Rhona born in Dundee – 1965, 1967 or 1969?

602. Which reality TV show was Rhona a contestant during 2002?

603. Following on from the previous question, in which position did Rhona finish out of the eight contestants – fourth, fifth or sixth?

604. What was the name of the BBC 2 sitcom that Rhona co-wrote and starred in during 2000?

605. In 2007 her debut novel 'The Naked Drinking Club' was published, but can you name the title of Rhona's book, about growing up as a lesbian in a small fishing port?

606. On which reality TV show did Rhona appear during June 2009?

607. Following on from the previous question, can you name the profession of Rhona's girlfriend Susan Dickson?

608. With which comedian and entertainer did Rhona spend time in his home during her time on the reality TV series during June 2009?

609. In 2002 which West End cast did Rhona join?

610. True or false: In 1992, Rhona became the first and the last woman to date to win So You Think You're Funny at the Edinburgh Fringe Festival?

THE X FACTOR – 2008

611. Which female singer won this show?

612. Following on from the previous question, who was the winner's mentor?

613. Which former Spice Girl helped Dannii Minogue guest judge at her St. Tropez home during the visits to the judges' homes?

614. Which group finished the show's runners-up?

615. Who was the celebrity guest during week five of the live shows, with the contestants having to sing one of her songs?

616. Which male singer finished in third place?

617. After the completion of bootcamp, which category did Simon Cowell mentor?

618. Why was judge Dannii Minogue missing from some of the auditions?

619. How many people applied to audition during this series – 180,000, 182,000 or 184,000?

620. Who presented the show on ITV1?

HELL'S KITCHEN – 2009

621. In which month in 2009 was this realty TV show made and broadcast?

622. Which female presenter presented the show, taking over from Angus Deayton?

623. Which former Dynasty actress won the show?

624. Can you name five of the eight celebrity contestants?

625. Can you name the former professional goalkeeper who was a contestant on the show?

626. How long did the series last – 13 days, 14 days or 15 days?

627. Who were the first two celebrities who were waiters (in the first episode)?

628. Who was the head chef?

629. Was this the – third series, fourth series or fifth series of the show?

630. Which channel was this show broadcast – BBC2, ITV or Channel 4?

BLIND DATE

631. In which year was the shown on television – 1983, 1984 or 1985?

632. Who presented the show?

633. Following on from the previous question, can you name the comedian who presented the show in the first pilot show?

634. True or false: In a Comic Relief special in 1993 Mr. Bean appeared on the show?

635. Who would Cilla ask for a quick reminder before Tommy Sandhu took over in the final series?

636. How many questions would the men or women have to answer by the opposite sex?

637. Which channel was this show broadcast – BBC1, BBC2 or ITV?

638. How many series were made on this show – 18, 19 or 20?

639. True or false: Future actress Amanda Holden appeared on the show in 1990?

640. In which year was this last shown on television then taken off the screens – 2003, 2004 or 2005?

CELEBRITY BIG BROTHER – SERIES 3

641. Where did a percentage of the phone vote funds go to?

642. In which month during 2005 was this show made?

643. Which Happy Mondays member won the show?

644. Which Australian journalist and feminist walked out of the house on day six?

645. True or false: Sylvester Stallone's mother was a housemate in this series?

646. Which charity was Caprice supporting during her time on the show?

647. Who entered the house on his 19th birthday and was also the show runner-up?

648. How many days did the show last – 16, 17 or 18?

649. True or false: Lisa I'Anson was booed heavily by the crowd on her exit from the house?

650. How much was the prize money which was donated to the DEC Tsunami Earthquake Appeal by the winner?

SURVIVOR – SERIES 2

651.   In which year was the second series broadcast?

652.   What were the names of the two islands?

653.   How old was Dave Porter, a retired fire fighter, he was the oldest contestant during the second series?

654.   What was the name of the merged tribe?

655.   Can you name the 30-year-old police detective who won this reality TV show?

656.   How many contestants were there during this series?

657.   Can you name the show that was aired on ITV2 once this show had finished, showing extra footage?

658.   True or false: There has only ever been two series of Survivor?

659.   Who presented this reality TV show during the second series, replacing Mark Austin and John Leslie from the first series?

660.   Can you name the teacher that finished runner-up in this reality TV show?

BIG BROTHER – SERIES 7

661. What was the prize money for this series - £70,000, £100,000 or £120,000?

662. How many housemates were there during this series?

663. Who won the show during 2006?

664. Can you name the housemate who entered the house through a 'golden ticket' promotion with Nestle?

665. What job did Glyn Wise do before entering the Big Brother house?

666. Which female contestant during this year was crowned Miss Wales in 2003?

667. Can you name the first contestant to leave the house, leaving in the first week?

668. True or false: In week six the housemates had to rub another housemate with soap until all of the soap was gone?

669. How many days did this series last – 91 days, 92 days or 93 days?

670. Which contestant finished third?

I'M A CELEBRITY GET ME OUT OF HERE – SERIES 8

671. Which former EastEnders actor won the show?

672. Can you name the two contestants that entered the jungle on day five?

673. Who was the first contestant to get voted out of the jungle?

674. Where did Martina Navratilova finish – runner-up, third or fourth?

675. On which day did Nicola McLean leave the jungle – day18, day 19 or day 20?

676. In which two months during 2008 was this reality TV show broadcast?

677. Which celebrity did the trials 'John Trevolting' and 'Jungle Gym' in weeks five and six?

678. What was the name of the trial Martina Navratilova did during the final day at the jungle?

679. Which celebrity did the most Bushtucker Trials during their stay in the jungle, with a total of seven trials?

680. Which band member of pop band Blue left the jungle on day 19?

BRITAIN'S GOT TALENT – SERIES 2

681. Which street dancer won the show?

682. Following on from the previous question, how old was the winner?

683. Who presented 'Britain's Got More Talent'?

684. In which year was series 2 made and broadcast?

685. True or false: The show had auditions at Blackpool for the first time?

686. On which TV channel was this show broadcast?

687. True or false: This show averaged over 10 million viewers per show?

688. Can you name the finalist, the 12-year-old classical singer from Kettering?

689. Can you name the three judges on the show?

690. Which dance group finished the show's runner-ups?

THE APPRENTICE – 2008

691. Who won the show?

692. How many applications did the producers of the show receive – 10,000, 20,000 or 30,000?

693. Can you name Alan Sugar's boardroom receptionist?

694. Who worked as a Risk Manager before she appeared on this show?

695. Lindi Mngaza was the youngest contestant on the show this year, how old was she – 21, 22 or 23?

696. What names did the teams call themselves before the first task?

697. Which chef cooked the winners' dinner when they won the first task in the first week?

698. Who was the show's runner-up?

699. What task did the teams have to do in the final week?

700. Which contestant was the first to be fired by Sir Alan?

JOE McELDERRY

701. Who was Joe's mentor during the live shows on the X Factor 2009?

702. With which celebrity performer did Joe sing during the finals on 12 December 2009?

703. In which year was Joe born – 1990, 1991 or 1992?

704. What is the name of Joe's debut single, released when he won the X Factor?

705. Which Robbie Williams song did Joe sing on the first live X Factor show?

706. Can you name the three other X Factor 2009 semi-finalists that Joe beat to be crowned the winner of the sixth series?

707. Which Michael Jackson song did Joe and the other X Factor finalists record for charity, going straight in at number one in the UK charts during 2009?

708. Which Luther Vandross song did Joe sing in his first audition in Manchester, which was televised in August 2009?

709. True or false: Joe previously auditioned for The X Factor in 2007?

710. Where in the UK is Joe from – South Shields, Sheffield or Stockport?

SIMON COWELL

711. What is Simon's middle name – Phillip, Peter or Paul?

712. It was reported that Simon appeared on which game show during 1990?

713. Simon is the godfather to which pop star's adopted children?

714. On which re-launched show was Simon a victim during 2007 when he was presented with a red book by Sir Trevor McDonald while on American Idol?

715. In 2003, which film did Simon make a cameo appearance as himself, getting killed by gunfire for criticising the act?

716. True or false: Simon was a judge on the first series of Pop Idol in 2001, and on the first series of American Idol in 2002?

717. Can you name the two judges Simon sat beside in 2004 in the first series of The X Factor?

718. Who won the third series of The X Factor and then signed to Simon's label Syco and went on to become an international star, with number one singles and album sales around the world?

719. Simon's record company signed which winner and runner-up of the first series of Pop Idol?

720. True or false: Simon's voice has featured in an episode of The Simpsons?

CELEBRITY BIG BROTHER – SERIES 4

721. In which month during 2006 was this show made and broadcast on Channel 4?

722. Which non-celebrity won the show?

723. Following on from the previous question, which musician did she meet in the Big Brother house and marry just months after the show?

724. Which former Football Association secretary was a housemate during this series?

725. Can you name the two housemates who received the most votes whilst in the house, with 10 each?

726. How many celebrities entered the Big Brother house during this series?

727. Who was the first celebrity to be evicted, after day nine?

728. Which comedian and former game show host finished the show's runner up?

729. Can you name the former American professional National Basketball Association player who was a contestant on the show?

730. Who did the housemates have to work for during a task on day 18 – Big Brother Bank, Big Brother Ice-cream Factory or Big Brother Hot Dogs?

HEAR'SAY

731.   Can you name the original five band members?

732.   Which reality TV show did the band members win in February 2001?

733.   What was Hear'say's first single?

734.   True or false: Before finding fame with Hear'say Danny Foster appeared on the Michael Barrymore music quiz show My Kind of Music as a contestant?

735.   Who replaced Kym Marsh in the band when she left in 2002?

736.   Which band did the five unsuccessful finalists go on to form?

737.   Can you name the song that Hear'say released in 2002, with the highest UK chart position being number six?

738.   True or false: Hear'Say went on to appear in the successful ITV show Hear'Say It's Saturday in 2001?

739.   Can you name the titles of both Hear'say's albums, released in 2001?

740.   True or false: Hear'say's third single, 'Everybody' was a UK number one?

GORDON RAMSEY OBE

741. What is Gordon's middle name?

742. For which Scottish football team did Gordon have a trial in 1984?

743. In which year was Gordon awarded the OBE for services to the hospitality industry?

744. True or false: Gordon appeared on series three of Faking It during 2001 helping a burger flipper called Ed Devlin, learn the trade?

745. Which reality TV show did Gordon create and star in during 2004?

746. Gordon held the top spot on Top Gear's celebrity leader board, with a lap time of 1.46.38 until overtaken by which record producer?

747. Which charity was Gordon supporting when he ran the London marathon in April 2009?

748. In which TV sitcom did Gordon appear as a celebrity guest in its Christmas Special during 2007?

749. In which year was Gordon born in Scotland – 1964, 1965 or 1966?

750. Which television channel broadcasts Gordon Ramsey's show The F Word?

GINO D'ACAMPO

751. What nationality is Gino?

752. In which year was he crowned king of the celebrity jungle in I'm A Celebrity ... Get Me Out Of Here!

753. Following on from the previous question, why were Gino and fellow contestant Stuart Manning charged by the Australian police with animal cruelty?

754. What is Gino's occupation?

755. What is the name of Gino's book, released in 2010?

756. Can you name the London restaurant Gino worked in when he was 20 years old?

757. With which former Brookside actress did Gino star in a programme called Chef v Britain in 2005?

758. True or false: Gino's grandfather was a head chef for Costa Cruise Ships?

759. Gino is the owner of a leading supplier of Italian ingredients to the UK food industry, what is his company name?

760. In which year was Gino born – 1974, 1975 or 1976?

JOE MILLIONAIRE

761. How many episodes were made of this American reality TV show – 6, 16 or 61?

762. Which female won the show?

763. True or false: During its first series Joe Millionaire got 40 million US viewers?

764. The bachelor wasn't actually a millionaire, what was his occupation– a construction worker, an accountant or an author?

765. On which American TV channel was this show broadcast?

766. What was the name of the bachelor?

767. In which country was Joe Millionaire made and broadcast?

768. Who presented the show?

769. In which year was this show first broadcast?

770. What was name of the sequel that followed Joe Millionaire?

THE HILLS

771. During series 1 Lauren left Laguna Beach and moved where?

772. Who created this reality TV show?

773. In which year did this reality TV show first hit our screens, shown on MTV?

774. What is the name of the theme tune, sung by Natasha Bedingfield?

775. Who received her own spin-off from The Hills entitled The City, which was first shown in 2008?

776. Who did Lauren break up with during series 2?

777. Which birthday did Lauren celebrate in the first half of series 5 – 23rd, 24th or 25th?

778. Who is Spencer's sister?

779. What is Brody's surname?

780. Which series of the reality TV show was first broadcast between April and September 2009?

PETE BENNETT

781.   What is the title of Pete's autobiography, which was
        published in 2006?

782.   Which series of Big Brother did Pete win?

783.   In which year was Pete born – 1980, 1981 or 1982?

784.   True or false: Pete has Tourette syndrome?

785.   Where in England does Pete live – Brighton,
        Birmingham or Blackburn?

786.   What is the name of Pete's band with whom he played
        at Glastonbury 2007?

787.   With which Big Brother housemate did Pete date from
        leaving the house, lasting just over a month?

788.   With which percentage did Pete win Big Brother -
        61.2%, 62.2% or 63.2%?

789.   True or false: Pete unsuccessfully auditioned for the
        fifth series of Big Brother in 2004?

790.   What is Pete's middle name?

CELEBRITY BIG BROTHER – SERIES 5

791. In which year did this series take place – 2006, 2007 or 2008?

792. Can you name five of the 11 housemates that entered the house on day one?

793. Which 'Jackson' finished the show's runner-up?

794. Which celebrity housemate received a series record 13 nominations during his stay in the house?

795. What did Donny Tourette do in the first night when he entered the house?

796. Can you name the three housemates that entered the house on day three?

797. Which celebrity contestant was a columnist for the Sunday Mirror and also starred in the 2006 series of Celebrity Fit Club?

798. Why did Channel 4 receive over 3,000 complaints during the show?

799. Can you recall the three housemates that walked out of the show of their own accord during the series?

800. Can you name the housemate who won the show?

CAMERON STOUT

801.   Which series of Big Brother did Cameron win?

802.   In which year was Cameron born in the Orkneys –
        1970, 1971 or 1972?

803.   What relation is Cameron to television and radio
        presenter Julyan Sinclair?

804.   With how many votes did Cameron win Big Brother –
        1.2 million, 1.9 million or 2.6 million?

805.   Who finished runner-up to Cameron in the Big Brother
        final?

806.   When Cameron won Big Brother, which museum
        opened an exhibition about his times in the house with
        objects such as his letter of acceptance and his suitcase
        on display?

807.   What job did Cameron do before winning Big Brother?

808.   Can you name the African Big Brother housemate that
        Cameron swapped places with for a two week period?

809.   True or false: Cameron said he was a virgin when he
        entered the Big Brother house in 2004?

810.   On day five in the Big Brother house, what did
        Cameron say he wouldn't do if someone offered him a
        million quid?

BIG BROTHER – SERIES 8

811.   Who won Big Brother in 2007?

812.   Can you name three of the five housemates that entered the house on day 59?

813.   How many contestants were there in total during series 8, more than any other previous series – 20, 22 or 24?

814.   Who was asked to leave the house on day nine after using a racially offensive word?

815.   Why were Chanelle and Ziggy restricted to only one nomination each during week seven?

816.   True or false: Liam finished in fourth place?

817.   How many days did this show last – 92 days, 94 days or 96 days?

818.   True or false: There was a fully-functioning washing machine hidden in the garden which was never found by any housemates?

819.   How many female contestants entered the house on the opening night, before Ziggy entered the house on day three?

820.   Can you name the twins that finished the show's runner-up?

I'M A CELEBRITY GET ME OUT OF HERE – SERIES 9

821. Who finished up as the show's runner-up to winner Gino D'Acampo?

822. How many days did the show last – 19, 20 or 21?

823. Which glamour model entered the jungle on day two and then left on day nine?

824. Following on from the previous question, how many Bushtucker Trials did she do whilst in the jungle during 2009?

825. Which girl pop band was contestant Sabrina Washington a former member?

826. Which professional snooker player finished in third place?

827. After how many days did Strictly Come Dancing professional dancer Camilla Dallerup leave the jungle?

828. Can you name the Bushtucker Trial in which Justin Ryan won eight out of eight stars, shown on 28 November 2009?

829. Following on from the previous question, can you name Justin's partner, who was a contestant, leaving after 11 days in the jungle?

830. Which Hollywood actor chose to leave the jungle on day 17?

STEVE BROOKSTEIN

831.   What is Steve's middle name – Desmond, Dennis or
        Daniel?

832.   What was the name of Steve's single that was released
        in 2004 which went to number 1 in the UK charts?

833.   True or false: Steve's first album 'Heart and Soul' went
        to number one in the UK album charts in 2005?

834.   In which year did Steve win The X Factor?

835.   Steve was in the over 25s' category, who was his
        mentor?

836.   Which band did Steve beat in The X Factor final?

837.   True or false: In 1997 Steve was a finalist on the ITV
        series The Big Big Talent Show presented by Jonathan
        Ross?

838.   How old was Steve when he won The X Factor – 26, 36
        or 46?

839.   Can you name Steve's second single which was
        released in 2006, the highest position being 193 in the
        UK charts?

840.   Where is Steve from – Bristol, Cardiff or London?

PETE WATERMAN OBE

841. What is the title of Pete's autobiography?

842. What is Pete's middle name?

843. On which TV show was Pete a judge between 2001 and 2003?

844. Following on from the previous question, which female singer and eventual winner, was Pete constantly critical of in 2003 during his time as a judge?

845. True or false: Pete is a very keen railway enthusiast?

846. In which Steps video did Pete appear?

847. In which year was Pete born – 1946, 1947 or 1948?

848. How many times has Pete been married?

849. Which rugby club is Pete the president of?

850. True or false: Pete was manager of the reality TV group One True Voice?

CELEBRITY BIG BROTHER – SERIES 6

851. In which month during 2009 was this show made and broadcast?

852. Which television presenter won this show?

853. Which 'Jackson' was a contestant on this year's show?

854. Who presented Big Brother's Big Mouth during this celebrity series?

855. Which band was contestant Michelle Heaton a former member of?

856. How many days did this show last – 18 days, 20 days or 22 days?

857. Which Scottish politician was a contestant on this year's show?

858. True or false: The winner actually received more nominations during her time in the house than anyone else?

859. Can you name six of the eleven contestants that entered the house on day one?

860. Which glamour model was the first housemate to be evicted?

CRAIG PHILLIPS

861. In which year was Craig born – 1969, 1970 or 1971?

862. Of which reality TV show did Craig win the first series?

863. Following on from the previous question, can you name Craig's friend to whom he gave his prize money?

864. Which TV show did Craig join and was in over 80 shows during 2008 and 2009?

865. True or false: Craig once released a Christmas single 'At This Time of Year'?

866. What is the name of Craig's autobiography, released in 2009?

867. True or false: Craig is a patron of the Down's Syndrome Association and a road safety charity called Brake?

868. On which TV show did Craig appear during February 2009?

869. Where in England was Craig born – Liverpool, London or Leeds?

870. On which reality TV show did Craig raise £40,000 for Macmillan Cancer Trust?

ALEXANDRA BURKE

871. How old was Alexandra when she won the fifth series of The X Factor?

872. With which song did Alexandra became the European record holder for single sales over a period of 24 hours, selling 105,000 copies of her debut single during December 2008?

873. What was Alexandra the first British female to do in music history in the UK?

874. Where in the UK is Alexandra from – London, Leeds or Liverpool?

875. Can you name the young Irish singer and the boy band that Alexandra beat in The X Factor final?

876. Alexandra auditioned in the second series of The X Factor in 2005, she made it to the final 21 in the 16-24 category, but who was in charge of this category – Simon Cowell, Sharon Osbourne or Louis Walsh?

877. Who was Alexandra's mentor during the 2008 success, when winning the show?

878. Following on from the previous question, can you name the other two contestants who were in the final three in the girls' category?

879. Which song did Alexandra sing as a duet with Beyoncé in The X Factor final?

880. In week nine of The X Factor Alexandra performed which Rhianna hit song?

TEMPTATION ISLAND

881. How many series were made of this reality television show?

882. In which year did this show first hit television screens in the USA?

883. Who presented the show?

884. Which American television company broadcast this show?

885. Can you name one of the two writers?

886. How many episodes were made during the show's life – 26, 29 or 32?

887. True or false: An Australian version of this show was also produced, and shown on the Seven Network?

888. Who appeared in series 1 and went on to be a part of the platinum-selling band Rehab's song 'More Like Me', followed by a solo music career?

889. In which location were the series filmed?

890. True or false: There has been an adaptation for CCTV in China?

MARCO PIERRE WHITE

891. True or false: Marco appeared in trailers for the 2004 film Layer Cake?

892. How many times has Marco been married – three, four or five?

893. Can you name the restaurant that Marco opened on the completion of his chef training in 1987?

894. What is the name of Marco's autobiography?

895. Which reality TV show did Marco start filming in 2007?

896. True or false: Marco is a dining consultant to the cruise line P&O Cruises?

897. In which year did Marco retire as a chef and cook his last meal for a paying customer at the Oak Room?

898. Can you name either two places that Marco started his chef training as a 16-year-old?

899. In which year was Marco born in Leeds – 1961, 1962 or 1963?

900. True or false: At the time, Marco was the youngest ever chef ever to have been awarded three Michelin stars?

NADIA ALMADA

901. In which year was Nadia born – 1976, 1977 or 1978?

902. For which bank did Nadia work as a cashier before entering the Big Brother house in 2004?

903. After winning Big Brother, Nadia released a music single, what was it called?

904. In 2005, which reality show shown on Channel 5 was Nadia a contestant?

905. With how many votes did Nadia win Big Brother in 2004 – 3.8 million, 4.8 million or 5.8 million?

906. What was Nadia's male name when she was born?

907. Following on from the previous question, in which year did Nadia undergo a sex change?

908. What prize did Nadia win when she won Big Brother in 2004 - £43,500, £53,500 or £63,500?

909. Nadia is the eldest of how many children – four, five or six?

910. What is Nadia's star sign – Aquarius, Gemini or Leo?

ANTHONY HUTTON

911. Which series of Big Brother was Anthony a contestant?

912. True or false: Anthony won Big Brother when he appeared in the show?

913. How old was Anthony when he entered the Big Brother house – 23, 25 or 27?

914. During the first nominations who was the only person to nominate Anthony?

915. Which job did Anthony do before he went into the Big Brother house?

916. Which hairdresser did Anthony become very good friends with whilst in the Big Brother house?

917. Which football team does Anthony support?

918. How many times did Anthony face eviction whilst in the Big Brother house – once, twice or three times?

919. True or false: Anthony was married when he walked into the Big Brother house?

920. Can you name the other three Big Brother finalists he was up against on the final day of the reality TV series?

BIG BROTHER – SERIES 9

921. Which female won this show in 2008?

922. Who was the only contestant to walk out of the show during this series?

923. How many days did this series last – 73, 83 or 93?

924. Can you name Rex's girlfriend who entered the house in week nine?

925. Who was elected the as the first 'head of house'?

926. Why were all the housemates evacuated from the house on day 32?

927. Which male contestant finished as the show's runner-up?

928. Can you name the two contestants who were a couple before they entered the house?

929. What job did Sara do before walking in the Big Brother house?

930. How old was Belinda when she entered the Big Brother house?

SCOTTISH REALITY TV CONTESTANTS

931. Can you name the Scottish X Factor finalist in 2006, she was mentored by Sharon Osbourne and was eliminated in the third week of the live shows along with Dionne Mitchell?

932. Which reality TV show did Edinburgh born John Loughton win during January 2008?

933. Which 36-year-old History of Art student from Aberdeen appeared as a contestant in Big Brother 3 and was the first housemate to face eviction after Sunita Sharma walked out of the house?

934. Can you name the Big Brother 9 contestant, a model from Fife?

935. Sharon McAllister was a contestant on which reality TV show during its second series?

936. Where in Scotland were The MacDonald Bros from, starring in The X Factor in 2006?

937. Who was the fourth housemate to be evicted in Big Brother 4, he was evicted during the double eviction night in the fourth week, having been nominated by Cameron, Gos, Jon, Nush and Steph?

938. Can you name the Big Brother 5 housemate from Glasgow who once won 'Mr Best Buttocks South Lanarkshire'?

939. How old was politician Tommy Sheridan when he entered the Celebrity Big Brother house in 2009?

940. Can you name the reality TV spin-off show that Glaswegian tycoon Michelle Mone regularly appeared in as a panelist/commentator?

THE X FACTOR – 2009

941. In which month during 2009 did the show start airing on ITV?

942. Can you name the three groups that Louis Walsh chose for the live shows?

943. True or false: Simon Cowell mentored the over 25s?

944. Can you name the three celebrity performers who performed with the final three in the final?

945. Which singer assisted Cheryl Cole in Marrakech, Morocco when contestants visited her house at the 'Judges' Houses' stage?

946. Can you name the identical twins from Ireland who were eliminated from the competition in week seven by the judges after being in the bottom two with Olly Murs?

947. Can you name the first of Simon Cowell's acts to go in the live shows, being eliminated in week six?

948. Who won this year's show beating Olly Murs in the final on Sunday 13 December 2009?

949. True or false: The contestants sang Take That and Elton John songs during week eight of the live shows?

950. Which female from Dagenham finished in third place?

DAVINA McCALL

951. In which year was Davina born – 1967, 1969 or 1971?

952. True or false: Davina presented the first 10 series of Big Brother?

953. Which dating game show did Davina present between 1998 and 2001?

954. True or false: Davina presented ITV's Popstars: The Rivals in 2002?

955. Which reality TV show did Davina present between 1998 and 2001 - Don't Try This At Home, The Friday Night Project or Eurotrash?

956. Can you name Davina's middle names?

957. Davina donated £50 for Red Rose Day 2009 for kissing which popular actor who co-hosted the show?

958. Can you name Davina's husband who she married in 2000, a former presenter of Pet Rescue?

959. What did Davina wear during her interview with Big Brother series 6 contestant Sam Heuston?

960. True or false: Davina's three children were all born in September of different years and she was pregnant during three different series of Big Brother?

AMERICA'S NEXT TOP MODEL

961. Which former model created this show?

962. Can you name the model that won the twelfth cycle during March 2009?

963. Where was the international destination during the show's first series during 2003?

964. Can you name the judge that judged from series 1 to series 4, she also appeared as a contestant on I'm a Celebrity ... Get Me Out Of Here...?

965. Which American TV channel broadcast this reality TV show from 2003 to 2006?

966. How many contestants were there during cycle two?

967. Who was the runner-up during cycle nine in September 2007?

968. Which Elle Magazine fashion editor was a judge on the show on its third and fourth cycle?

969. Can you name the model that won the fifth cycle during September 2005?

970. Where was the international destination during the show's seventh cycle during 2003?

KATE LAWLER

971. What is Kate's middle name – Louise, Lorna or Lisa?

972. Which series of Big Brother was Kate the winner?

973. Following on from the previous question, what was Kate the first to do?

974. Which Channel 4 breakfast TV show did Kate co-present in 2003?

975. Which football team does Kate support?

976. During April 2008, what did Kate do wearing only Ann Summers lingerie, raising funds for the Cystic Fibrosis Trust?

977. What reality TV series did Kate appear as a contestant during 2006?

978. Who did Kate beat in the Big Brother final – Alex, Jade or Jonny?

979. How old was Kate when she walked into the Big Brother house – 20, 22 or 24?

980. Which housemate in the Big Brother house was Kate talking about on day 11 when she said: 'He is fit as well, he is just so funny'?

BIG BROTHER – SERIES 10

981.   How many contestants entered the house during the 2009 show?

982.   Who was the oldest person to enter the house this year, at the age of 41?

983.   What did Sophie change her name to during the show and often got referred to as?

984.   Who finished the show's runner-up to Sophie?

985.   Who narrated the show?

986.   How many days did Big Brother last during series 10 – 91 days, 93 days or 95 days?

987.   Which Britain's Got Talent act appeared on Big Brother in week eight when housemates took part in a Greek-themed shopping task?

988.   Whose eyebrows got shaved off during the first evening of this series of Big Brother?

989.   Which housemate was often referred to as 'Halfwit'?

990.   How many cameras were used in the house during this series – 22, 33 or 44?

MICHELLE DEWBERRY

991. Where in the UK was Michelle born – Hull, Manchester or Nottingham?

992. When Michelle left school at 16, where was she appointed as an apprentice?

993. Which reality TV series was Michelle a contestant in the first series during 2006 aired on BBC Three?

994. Who did Michelle beat in The Apprentice final?

995. True or false: Michelle won the third series of The Apprentice?

996. Can you name one of the nicknames that was given to Michelle by the British press during her time on The Apprentice?

997. For which charity did Michelle run the London Marathon in 2007?

998. Can you name the title of Michelle's autobiography?

999. How long did Michelle work for Sir Alan Sugar – one year, two years or three and a half years?

1000. Why did Michelle leave Sir Alan Sugar's employment in 2006?

ANSWERS

BIG BROTHER – SERIES 1

1.   2000

2.   £70,000

3.   10

4.   Andrew, Anna, Caroline, Craig, Darren, Melanie, Nichola, Nicholas, Sada and Tom

5.   64 days

6.   True: The first task was for housemates to make a clay bowl and mug each using a potter's wheel, if more than three objects cracked when cooked, the housemates would fail.

7.   Anna Nolan

8.   True (with 20 nominations)

9.   51%

10.   Nicholas Bateman

I'M A CELEBRITY GET ME OUT OF HERE – SERIES 1

11.   2002

12.   Anthony McPartlin and Declan Donnelly (Ant and Dec)

13.   Tony Blackburn

14.   Eight

15.   Tara Palmer-Tomkinson

16.   Palazzo Versace Hotel at Southport

17.   Rhona Cameron

18.   Louise Loughman

19.   Uri Geller

20.   ITV

BRITAIN'S GOT TALENT – SERIES 3

21.   Susan Boyle

22.   The Priory

23.   April and May 2009

24. *Anthony McPartlin and Declan Donnelly (Ant and Dec)*

25. *Diversity*

26. *Kelly Brook*

27. *Britain's Got More Talent*

28. *The saxophone*

29. *24.9%*

30. *Hollie Steel*

JADE GOODY

31. *Third series*

32. *She was a dental nurse*

33. *Cerisa Lorraine*

34. *Jack Tweed*

35. *2008*

36. *Shh ... Jade Goody*

37. *NSPCC*

38. *Bobby and Freddie*

39. *1981*

40. *True*

THE APPRENTICE – 2009

41. *Fifth series*

42. *Mark Burnett*

43. *True*

44. *Nick Hewer and Margaret Mountford*

45. *Yasmina Siadatan*

46. *15 (there was meant to be 16 but one pulled out the day before filming began)*

47. *Yasmina, Kate, Debra, Lorraine, James, Howard, Ben, Phillip, Mona, Noorul, Kimberly, Paula, Majid, Rocky and Anita (and Adam who resigned before filming began)*

48. *A project manager*

49. *£100,000*

50. *'You're fired!'*

MATCH UP THE YEAR

51.	Holiday Showdown was first broadcast	2003
52.	The only series of Farmer Wants a Wife was broadcast	2001
53.	Blind Date was first broadcast	1985
54.	The Osbournes was first broadcast	2002
55.	Hogan Knows Best was first broadcast	2005
56.	Temptation Island was first broadcast	2001
57.	America's Next Top Model was first broadcast	2003
58.	Candid Camera was first broadcast	1948
59.	Survivor was first broadcast	2001
60.	The second series of Trinny & Susannah Undress... was broadcast	2007

WHICH CHANNEL?

61.	Wife Swap	Channel 4
62.	Top Chef	Bravo
63.	Average Joe	NBC
64.	Fat March	ABC
65.	Pop Idol	ITV
66.	The Osbournes	MTV
67.	American Idol	FOX
68.	The Restaurant	NBC
69.	The Hills	MTV
70.	Road Rules	MTV

BRIAN DOWLING

71. *True*

72. *Fáilte Towers*

73. *Gemini*

74. *Bambi*

75. *Big Brother 2*

76. *Hell's Kitchen*

77. *Captain Hook*

78. *True*

79. *Ryanair*

80. *1978*

THE X FACTOR – 2004

81. *True*

82. *Steve Brookstein*

83. *Against All Odds (Take a Look at Me Now)*

84. *G4*

85. *Louis Walsh*

86. *Cassie Compton, Roberta Howett and Tabby Callaghan*

87. *Kate Thornton*

88. *Simon Cowell*

89. *Saturday evening*

90. *Verity Keays*

HELL'S KITCHEN – 2004

91. *Gordon Ramsay*

92. *ITV*

93. *Jennifer Ellison*

94. *The blue team (but won being part of the white team)*

95. *Roger Cook*

96. *Hell's Kitchen: School Reunion*

97. *James Dreyfus*

98. *True: the UK version started in 2004 and the American version started in 2005*

99.   *Angus Deayton*

100.   *Edwina Currie*

DARIUS

101.   *Leo (born on 19 August 1980)*

102.   *Iranian*

103.   *Danesh*

104.   *Number one*

105.   *True*

106.   *Dive In*

107.   *2005*

108.   *Hotel Babylon*

109.   *Pop Idol*

110.   *Five*

BIG BROTHER – SERIES 2

111.   *Brian Dowling*

112.   *Amma, Brian, Bubble, Dean, Elizabeth, Helen, Narinder, Paul, Penny and Stuart*

113.   *They had to keep a fire burning in the garden for 120 hours*

114.   *She was a hairdresser*

115.   *Penny Ellis*

116.   *True*

117.   *Josh Rafter*

118.   *Bubble (Paul Ferguson)*

119.   *64 days*

120.   *Dean O'Loughlin*

I'M A CELEBRITY GET ME OUT OF HERE – SERIES 2

121.   *Phil Tufnell*

122.   *Siân Lloyd*

123. 2003

124. Linda Barker

125. 10

126. Chris Bisson

127. Second

128. Antony Worrall Thompson

129. April and May

130. Toyah Willcox

THE APPRENTICE – 2005

131. True

132. Tim (Timothy Campbell)

133. 14

134. The women chose the name First Forte for their team, while the men named their team Impact

135. Paul Torrisi

136. Buying and selling flowers

137. True

138. Saira

139. It was a marketing campaign for a text messaging service of football team news sent to fans' mobile phones

140. James, Paul, Saira and Tim

THE X FACTOR – 2005

141. Shayne Ward

142. Andy Abraham, Brenda Edwards, Chico Slimani and Maria Lawson

143. That's My Goal

144. True

145. Kate Thornton

146. Something About the Way You look Tonight

147. *Life Starts Now*

148. *10*

149. *The groups*

150. *Andy Abraham*

HELL'S KITCHEN – 2005

151. *Gary Rhodes and Jean-Christophe Novelli*

152. *£250,000 (with which the winner could start their own restaurant)*

153. *True*

154. *Angus Deayton*

155. *Series 2*

156. *Terry Miller, Simon Gross, Aaron Siwoku, Caroline Garvey and Sam Raplin*

157. *False*

158. *ITV*

159. *Terry Miller*

160. *Henry Filloux-Bennett, Aby King, Gary Tomlin, Kellie Cresswell and Stien Smart*

CELEBRITY WIFE SWAP

161. *Vanessa Feltz and her fiancé Ben Ofoedu*

162. *Pete Burns*

163. *John McCririck*

164. *False: He hasn't appeared on Celebrity Wife Swap*

165. *Sandra*

166. *Jeff Brazier*

167. *Charles and Diana Ingram*

168. *Myra Strattan*

169. *True*

170. *Jilly and Paul Goolden*

LEONA LEWIS

171.   Louise

172.   True

173.   Over the Rainbow

174.   Dreams

175.   True

176.   1985

177.   Spirit

178.   True

179.   Bleeding Love

180.   London

KATIE AND PETER

181.   1978

182.   Sarah Harding

183.   The Friday Night Project

184.   True

185.   Jordan

186.   James

187.   I'm a Celebrity... Get Me Out of Here!

188.   Celebrity Mum of the Year

189.   Mysterious Girl

190.   2009

POP IDOL – SERIES 1

191.   Simon Fuller

192.   Zoe Birkett (4th) and Hayley Evetts (5th)

193.   Will Young

194.   Gareth Gates

195.   2001

196.   True

197. *Pop Idol Extra*

198. *Saturday*

199. *Darius Danesh*

200. *True*

MICHELLE McMANUS

201. *True*

202. *Loose Women*

203. *1980*

204. *Hey Jude*

205. *Just For You*

206. *She was an events manager for Marriott Hotels in Glasgow*

207. *6.5 million*

208. *The Meaning Of Love*

209. *On The Radio*

210. *True*

BIG BROTHER – SERIES 3

211. *May, June and July*

212. *Sunita (after seven days) and Sandy (after 20 days)*

213. *12*

214. *Day 51*

215. *He was a personal trainer*

216. *Newcastle*

217. *They discussed nominations*

218. *The house was split into to sides (a rich side and a poor side)*

219. *False: She came fourth*

220. *Lee and Sophie*

I'M A CELEBRITY GET ME OUT OF HERE – SERIES 3

221. *Kerry Katona*

222. *2004 (January and February)*

223. *Neil Ruddock*

224. *Lord Brocket*

225. *George Best*

226. *Diane Modahl*

227. *BBC*

228. *10*

229. *Peter André*

230. *Mike Read*

THE APPRENTICE – 2006

231. *BBC2*

232. *Karen Bremner*

233. *They sold fruit and vegetables in Hackney, London*

234. *Michelle Dewberry*

235. *Ruth Badger*

236. *True*

237. *Second series*

238. *Sharon McAllister*

239. *True*

240. *Ansell, Michelle, Paul and Ruth*

THE X FACTOR – 2006

241. *August*

242. *Kate Thornton*

243. *Simon Cowell*

244. *Ray Quinn*

245. *Louis Walsh*

246. *Take That and Westlife*

247. *Anthony Hannah, Danny Morris, David Heath and James Edwards*

248. *A Moment Like This*

249. *Paula Abdul*

250. *Robert Allen, Kerry McGregor, Ben Mills and Dionne Mitchell*

CELEBRITY BIG BROTHER – SERIES 1

251. *Comic Relief*

252. *Six*

253. *Jack Dee*

254. *Chris Eubank (five nominations) and Anthea Turner (three nominations)*

255. *Keith Duffy*

256. *Vanessa Feltz*

257. *March*

258. *Claire Sweeney*

259. *Chris Eubank*

260. *Eight*

RACHEL RICE

261. *1984*

262. *Night Train to Venice*

263. *Series 9*

264. *Michael*

265. *The Sunday Night Project*

266. *True*

267. *Lisa and Rex*

268. *Alexandra and Sylvia*

269. *21*

270. *True*

CELEBRITY BIG BROTHER – SERIES 7

271. *Vinnie Jones*

272. *Katia and Heidi*

273. Ivana Trump

274. To fit inside a Mini

275. Alex Reid, Dane Bowers, Heidi Fleiss, Jonas Altberg, Katia Ivanova, Lady Sovereign, Nicola Tappenden, Sisqó, Stephanie Beacham, Stephen Baldwin and Vinnie Jones

276. 27 days

277. Page 3 Girl and glamour model

278. Davina McCall

279. Dane Bowers

280. Alex Reid

WILL YOUNG

281. Robert

282. Pop Idol

283. Blame It on the Boogie

284. Let It Go

285. 2003

286. Elton John

287. True

288. Over one million

289. Cheryl Cole

290. 1979

SHAYNE WARD

291. Thomas

292. 2005

293. Manchester United

294. True

295. That's My Goal

296. True

297. Breathless

298.   *1984*

299.   *Louis Walsh*

300.   *Breathless*

SURVIVOR – SERIES 1

301.   *Charlotte Hobrough*

302.   *ITV*

303.   *2001*

304.   *£1 million*

305.   *16*

306.   *True*

307.   *Pulau Tiga, Malaysia*

308.   *Helang (Eagle) and Ular (Snake)*

309.   *6.6 million*

310.   *Jackie Carey*

I'M A CELEBRITY GET ME OUT OF HERE – SERIES 4

311.   *2004*

312.   *Sophie Anderton*

313.   *Joe Pasquale*

314.   *Brian Harvey*

315.   *Paul Burrell*

316.   *November and December*

317.   *Seven stars*

318.   *Nancy Sorrell (Natalie Appleton and Brian Harvey withdrew before this)*

319.   *11*

320.   *Fran Cosgrave*

THE APPRENTICE – 2007

321.   *Simon Ambrose*

322. *27*

323. *Kristina Grimes*

324. *Coffee*

325. *Andy Jackson*

326. *Twice (in weeks seven and 10)*

327. *London Zoo*

328. *Eclipse and Stealth*

329. *June*

330. *Tre Azam*

SIR ALAN SUGAR

331. *Michael*

332. *Amstrad*

333. *Tottenham Hotspur*

334. *Mopsy (because of his hair)*

335. *Rita Simons (playing character Roxy Mitchell)*

336. *For his services to business*

337. *2005*

338. *Ann*

339. *Hackney in East London*

340. *Amstrad (the company name being an acronym of his initials: Alan Michael Sugar Trading)*

REBECCA LOOS

341. *Spain*

342. *The Farm*

343. *True*

344. *Calum Best*

345. *British Red Cross*

346. *Your Boyfriend*

347. *2004*

348. *The Podge and Rodge Show*

349. *True*

350. *Dream Team*

LEON JACKSON

351. *1988*

352. *Gap*

353. *True*

354. *Dannii Minogue*

355. *Kylie Minogue*

356. *2007*

357. *The biggest shock in the history of reality TV betting*

358. *Stargazing*

359. *Michael Bublé*

360. *When You Believe*

BIG BROTHER – SERIES 4

361. *Anouska Golebiewski*

362. *Cameron Stout*

363. *Ray Shah*

364. *Gos*

365. *Jon Tickle*

366. *£70,000*

367. *True*

368. *Federico and Jon*

369. *She was a shop manager*

370. *Six*

THE X FACTOR – 2007

371. *Leon Jackson*

372. *True*

373. *Dermot O'Leary*

374. *Three*

375. *Brian Friedman*

376. *True*

377. *The groups*

378. *Nicole Scherzinger*

379. *When You Believe*

380. *Rhydian Roberts*

SOPHIE ANDERTON

381. *Bristol*

382. *2006*

383. *True*

384. *Popcorn*

385. *Cold Turkey*

386. *2006*

387. *Me-Me*

388. *Hole in the Wall*

389. *I'm A Celebrity ... Get Me Out Of Here...!*

390. *Natalie Appleton*

CELEBRITY BIG BROTHER – SERIES 2

391. *Mark Owen*

392. *2002*

393. *Six*

394. *Goldie*

395. *Melinda Messenger*

396. *Centrepoint, National Missing Persons Helpline, Rethink and Samaritans*

397. *O2*

398. *Sue Perkins*

399.	Anne Diamond

400.	10

GARETH GATES

401.	1984

402.	Pop Idol

403.	Suzanne

404.	True

405.	Maria Filippov

406.	Simon Cowell

407.	False: the highest UK position in the charts was number three

408.	Unchained Melody

409.	True

410.	Paul

CELEBRITY LOVE ISLAND/LOVE ISLAND

411.	2005

412.	Atomic Kitten

413.	Rebecca Loos

414.	Lee Sharpe

415.	Fiji

416.	Wish I

417.	Kéllé Bryan

418.	£50,000

419.	Bianca Gascoigne and Calum Best

420.	True

I'M A CELEBRITY GET ME OUT OF HERE – SERIES 5

421.	18

422.	Sheree Murphy

423.	12

424. *Kimberley Davies*

425. *True*

426. *Antony Costa*

427. *Carol Thatcher and Sid Owen*

428. *Jimmy Osmond*

429. *2005*

430. *Carol Thatcher*

THE OSBOURNES

431. *True*

432. *Aimee*

433. *Crazy Train*

434. *Because he was stoned during the entire filming of The Osbournes*

435. *Kelly: she was born in 1984 and Jack was born in 1985*

436. *Beverly Hills*

437. *Oliver Stone*

438. *John Michael Osbourne*

439. *Lola*

440. *She is their nanny*

BIG BROTHER – SERIES 5

441. *12*

442. *Nadia Almada*

443. *Kitten*

444. *Michelle Bass*

445. *London*

446. *Michelle and Emma*

447. *Ahmed*

448. *Jason*

449. *Becki*

450.   *2004*

CHANTELLE HOUGHTON

451.   *1983*

452.   *True*

453.   *Living the Dream*

454.   *Call me a Cabbie*

455.   *Vivien*

456.   *True*

457.   *7*

458.   *2006*

459.   *10 months*

460.   *True*

ANT AND DEC

461.   *Anthony McPartlin and Declan Donnelly*

462.   *Byker Grove*

463.   *PJ & Duncan*

464.   *Dec: He was born in September 1975 (Ant was born in November 1975)*

465.   *True*

466.   *Newcastle United*

467.   *Ooh! What a Lovely Pair. Our Story*

468.   *Britain's Got Talent*

469.   *PokerFace*

470.   *True*

POP IDOL – SERIES 2

471.   *Michelle McManus*

472.   *All This Time*

473.   *2003*

474.   *ITV*

475. *Christmas songs*

476. *16-26*

477. *Ant and Dec*

478. *Sam Nixon*

479. *Simon Cowell, Neil Fox, Nicki Chapman and Pete Waterman*

480. *Mark Rhodes*

AMERICAN IDOL

481. *American Idol: The Search for a Superstar*

482. *2002*

483. *Kelly Clarkson*

484. *False*

485. *Nigel Lythgoe*

486. *Simon Fuller*

487. *Taylor Hicks*

488. *ITV2*

489. *Paula Abdul*

490. *Kris Allen*

HOGAN KNOWS BEST

491. *Nick and Brooke*

492. *Brooke-tini*

493. *Four*

494. *Terry Bollea*

495. *Brooke Knows Best*

496. *Brian Knobbs*

497. *A former professional wrestling legend*

498. *Socko (Hogan Energy Powered by Socko)*

499. *2005*

500. *True*

GIRLS ALOUD

501.	Cheryl Cole, Nadine Coyle, Sarah Harding, Nicola Roberts, and Kimberley Walsh

502.	2002

503.	The Promise

504.	Most Successful Reality TV Group

505.	True

506.	Davina McCall

507.	One True Voice

508.	Sound of the Underground

509.	Can't Speak French, The Promise and The Loving Kind

510.	Chemistry

CANDID CAMERA

511.	1947

512.	Allen Funt

513.	Peter Funt

514.	True

515.	38

516.	1948

517.	True

518.	Smile, You're on Candid Camera!

519.	Dorothy Collins

520.	True

THE CELEBRITY APPRENTINCE

521.	Comic Relief

522.	The Women's team

523.	True

524.	Sport Relief

525.	Kirstie Allsopp, Clare Balding, Jacqueline Gold, Louise Redknapp and Lisa Snowdon

526. **Hardeep Singh Kohli**

527. **Rupert Everett**

528. **False: she never appeared on this show**

529. **Jonathan Ross**

530. **Alan Carr**

COACH TRIP

531. **Chris Groombridge**

532. **Brendan Sheerin**

533. **London**

534. **True**

535. **Maggie and Paul**

536. **30 days**

537. **Paul and Joy**

538. **David Quantick**

539. **Munich**

540. **Geoff and Anne**

CHRISTOPHER BIGGINS

541. **1948**

542. **Lukewarm**

543. **Beatrice Norbury**

544. **Lesley Joseph**

545. **True**

546. **Some Mothers Do 'Ave 'Em**

547. **Psychoville**

548. **Biggins**

549. **Neil Sinclair**

550. **True**

I'M A CELEBRITY GET ME OUT OF HERE – SERIES 6

551. **Matt Willis**

552. **Toby Anstis**

553. **True**

554. **2006**

555. **Malandra Burrows**

556. **One**

557. **Jan Leeming**

558. **True (Toby Anstis didn't do any either)**

559. **Myleene Klass and Jason Donovan**

560. **Dean Gaffney**

GEORGE GALLOWAY

561. **Fourth series**

562. **Eighth**

563. **I'm Not The Only One**

564. **1987**

565. **Dundee**

566. **True**

567. **Chantelle Houghton and Dennis Rodman**

568. **InterPal**

569. **Respect – The Unity Coalition**

570. **Bethnal Green and Bow**

BIG BROTHER – SERIES 6

571. **16**

572. **Anthony Hutton**

573. **He was a hair stylist**

574. **Orlaith McAllister**

575. **Because nominations had been discussed for the third time**

576. **Eugene**

577. **Russell Brand**

578. **Day 29**

579. Kinga Karolczak, Orlaith McAllister and Eugene Sully

580. Saskia

I'M A CELEBRITY GET ME OUT OF HERE – SERIES 7

581. Day five

582. November

583. Janice Dickinson

584. Croc Creek and Snake Rock

585. Rodney Marsh

586. Wheel of Misfortune

587. Katie Hopkins

588. Malcolm McLaren

589. Five

590. Gemma Atkinson

BRITAINS GOT TALENT – SERIES 1

591. 2007

592. Paul Potts

593. Connie Talbot

594. Simon Cowell, Amanda Holden and Piers Morgan

595. 11 million

596. Damon Scott

597. True

598. Paul Potts, Connie Talbot, Damon Scott, Bessie Cursons, Kombat Breakers and The Bar Wizards

599. ITV

600. One Chance

RHONA CAMERON

601. 1965

602. I'm a Celebrity... Get Me out of Here!

603. Fifth

604. Rhona

605. Nineteen Seventy-Nine: A Big Year in a Small Town

606. Celebrity Wife Swap

607. She is a schoolteacher

608. Stan Boardman

609. The Vagina Monologues

610. True

THE X FACTOR – 2008

611. Alexandra Burke

612. Cheryl Cole

613. Emma Bunton

614. JLS

615. Mariah Carey

616. Eoghan Quigg

617. The Boys

618. Due to visits to Australia in order to film auditions for Australia's Got Talent

619. 182,000

620. Dermot O'Leary

HELL'S KITCHEN – 2009

621. April

622. Claudia Winkleman

623. Linda Evans

624. Adrian Edmondson, Anthea Turner, Bruce Grobbelaar, Danielle Bux, Grant Bovey, Jody Latham, Linda Evans and Niomi McLean-Daley (Ms. Dynamite)

625. Bruce Grobbelaar

626. 15 days (15 episodes)

627.   Adrian and Linda

628.   Marco Pierre White

629.   Series 4

630.   ITV

BLIND DATE

631.   1985

632.   Cilla Black

633.   Duncan Norvelle

634.   True

635.   Graham Skidmore

636.   Three

637.   ITV

638.   18

639.   True

640.   2003

CELEBRITY BIG BROTHER – SERIES 3

641.   To help victims of the 2004 Indian Ocean earthquake

642.   January

643.   Bez

644.   Germaine Greer

645.   True: Jackie Stallone entered the house on day five

646.   ChildLine

647.   Kenzie

648.   18

649.   True

650.   £50,000

SURVIVOR – SERIES 2

651.   2002

652. *South Island and North Island*

653. *55*

654. *Columbus*

655. *Jonny Gibb*

656. *12*

657. *Survivor: Raw*

658. *True: Series two was the last one*

659. *Mark Nicholas*

660. *Susannah Moffatt*

BIG BROTHER – SERIES 7

661. *£100,000*

662. *22*

663. *Pete Bennett*

664. *Susie Verrico*

665. *A swimming pool lifeguard*

666. *Imogen Thomas*

667. *Bonnie*

668. *True*

669. *93*

670. *Aisleyne*

I'M A CELEBRITY GET ME OUT OF HERE – SERIES 8

671. *Joe Swash*

672. *David Van Day and Timmy Mallett*

673. *Robert Kilroy-Silk*

674. *Runner-up*

675. *Day 18*

676. *November and December*

677. *Robert Kilroy-Silk*

678. *Fill Your Face*

679.   Joe Swash

680.   Simon Webbe

BRITAIN'S GOT TALENT – SERIES 2

681.   George Sampson

682.   14

683.   Stephen Mulhern

684.   2008

685.   True

686.   ITV

687.   True

688.   Faryl Smith

689.   Simon Cowell, Amanda Holden and Piers Morgan

690.   Signature

THE APPRENTICE – 2008

691.   Lee McQueen

692.   20,000

693.   Frances

694.   Lucinda Ledgerwood

695.   22

696.   Alpha and Renaissance

697.   Jean-Christophe Novelli

698.   Claire Young

699.   They had to develop an original fragrance for men

700.   Nicholas de Lacy-Brown

JOE McELDERRY

701.   Cheryl Cole

702.   George Michael

703.   1991

704.   *The Climb*

705.   *No Regrets*

706.   *Olly Murs, Danyl Johnson and Stacey Solomon*

707.   *You Are Not Alone*

708.   *Dance With My Father*

709.   *True*

710.   *South Shields, Tyne and Wear*

SIMON COWELL

711.   *Phillip*

712.   *Sale of the Century*

713.   *Sinitta*

714.   *This Is Your Life*

715.   *Scary Movie 3*

716.   *True*

717.   *Sharon Osbourne and Louis Walsh*

718.   *Leona Lewis*

719.   *Will Young and Gareth Gates*

720.   *True: In an episode titled 'Smart and Smarter'*

CELEBRITY BIG BROTHER – SERIES 4

721.   *January*

722.   *Chantelle Houghton*

723.   *Preston*

724.   *Faria Alam*

725.   *George Galloway and Pete Burns*

726.   *11*

727.   *Jodie Marsh*

728.   *Michael Barrymore*

729.   *Dennis Rodman*

730.   *Big Brother Bank*

HEAR'SAY

731.   Danny Foster, Myleene Klass, Kym Marsh, Suzanne Shaw and
         Noel Sullivan

732.   Popstars

733.   Pure and Simple

734.   True

735.   Johnny Shentall

736.   Liberty (then Liberty X due to legal reasons)

737.   Lovin' Is Easy

738.   True

739.   Popstars and Everybody

740.   False: The highest UK position was number four

GORDON RAMSEY OBE

741.   James

742.   Glasgow Rangers

743.   2006

744.   True

745.   Hell's Kitchen

746.   Simon Cowell

747.   Scottish Spina Bifida Association

748.   Extras

749.   1966

750.   Channel 4

GINO D'ACAMPO

751.   Italian

752.   2009

753.   For killing and cooking a rat on the show

754.   Chef

755.   The Italian Diet

756.   The Orchard Restaurant

757. *Claire Sweeney*

758. *True*

759. *Bontà Italia Ltd*

760. *1976*

JOE MILLIONAIRE

761. *Six*

762. *Zora Andrich*

763. *True*

764. *A construction worker*

765. *FOX*

766. *Evan Marriott*

767. *France*

768. *Alex McLeod*

769. *2003*

770. *The Next Joe Millionaire*

THE HILLS

771. *Los Angeles*

772. *Adam DiVello*

773. *2006*

774. *Unwritten*

775. *Whitney Port*

776. *Jason*

777. *23rd*

778. *Stephanie*

779. *Jenner*

780. *Series 5*

PETE BENNETT

781. *Pete: My Story*

782. *Big Brother 7*

783. *1982*

784. *True*

785. *Brighton*

786. *Pete Bennett and the Love Dogs*

787. *Nikki Grahame*

788. *61.2%*

789. *True*

790. *Alexander*

CELEBRITY BIG BROTHER – SERIES 5

791. *2007*

792. *Carole, Cleo, Danielle, Dirk, Donny, Ian, Jermaine, Jo, Ken, Leo, and Shilpa*

793. *Jermaine Jackson*

794. *Dirk*

795. *He jumped into the Jacuzzi fully clothed*

796. *Jack, Jackiey, and Jade*

797. *Carole Malone*

798. *The complaints were about racism and bullying by housemates against Shilpa Shetty (The UK media regulator Ofcom actually received over 44,500 complaints which is a record number for a British television programme after transmission)*

799. *Donny Tourette, Ken Russell and Leo Sayer*

800. *Shilpa Shetty*

CAMERON STOUT

801. *Series 4*

802. *1971*

803. *They are brothers (Cameron being the older one)*

804. *1.9 million*

805. *Ray Shah*

806. *Stromness Museum*

807. *A fish trader*

808. *Gaetano Kagwa*

809. *True*

810. *Take drugs*

BIG BROTHER – SERIES 8

811. *Brian Belo*

812. *Amy, Jonty, Shanessa, David and Kara-Louise*

813. *24*

814. *Emily*

815. *For discussing nominations*

816. *False: He finished in third place*

817. *94 days*

818. *True*

819. *11*

820. *Amanda and Sam*

I'M A CELEBRITY GET ME OUT OF HERE – SERIES 9

821. *Kim Woodburn*

822. *21 days*

823. *Katie Price*

824. *Six*

825. *Mis-Teeq*

826. *Jimmy White*

827. *Four days*

828. *Great Barrier Grief*

829. *Colin McAllister*

830. *George Hamilton*

STEVE BROOKSTEIN

831.   Desmond

832.   Against All Odds

833.   True

834.   2004

835.   Simon Cowell

836.   G4

837.   True

838.   36

839.   Fighting Butterflies

840.   London

PETE WATERMAN OBE

841.   I Wish I Was Me: The Autobiography

842.   Alan

843.   Pop Idol

844.   Michelle McManus

845.   True

846.   Tragedy

847.   1947

848.   Three

849.   Coventry Bears

850.   True

CELEBRITY BIG BROTHER – SERIES 6

851.   January

852.   Ulrika Jonsson

853.   La Toya Jackson

854.   Jack Whitehall

855.   Liberty X

856.   22 days

857.   Tommy Sheridan

858. True (she received 11 throughout the show)

859. La Toya, Mutya, Verne, Tommy, Lucy, Ben, Tina, Coolio, Michelle, Terry and Ulrika

860. Lucy Pinder

CRAIG PHILLIPS

861. 1971

862. Big Brother

863. Joanne Harris

864. 60 Minute Makeover

865. True

866. My Story: Building Beyond Big Brother

867. True

868. Ant and Dec's Saturday Night Takeaway

869. Liverpool

870. Back To Reality

ALEXANDRA BURKE

871. 20

872. Hallelujah

873. She was the first British female solo artist to sell a million copies of a single in the UK (with sales of 'Hallelujah' passing one million copies in January 2009)

874. London (Islington)

875. Eoghan Quigg and JLS

876. Louis Walsh

877. Cheryl Cole

878. Diana Vickers and Laura White

879. Listen

880. Don't Stop the Music

TEMPTATION ISLAND

881.   Three

882.   2001

883.   Mark L. Walberg

884.   FOX

885.   Aliyah Silverstein and Brendan Wentworth

886.   26

887.   True

888.   Mandy Lauderdale

889.   Ambergris Caye, Belize

890.   True

MARCO PIERRE WHITE

891.   True

892.   Three

893.   Harveys in Wandsworth Common

894.   White Slave

895.   Hell's Kitchen

896.   True

897.   1999

898.   Hotel St George in Harrogate, North Yorkshire and at the Box
       Tree in Ilkley, West Yorkshire

899.   1961

900.   True

NADIA ALMADA

901.   1977

902.   Barclays

903.   A Little Bit Of Action

904.   Trust Me...I'm A Holiday Rep

905.   3.8 million votes

906.	Jorge Leodoro
907.	2003
908.	£63,500
909.	Six
910.	Aquarius

ANTHONY HUTTON

911.	Big Brother 6
912.	True
913.	23
914.	Makosi
915.	He was a 1970s' dancer
916.	Craig Coates
917.	Newcastle United
918.	Once
919.	False: He was single
920.	Eugene, Kinga and Makosi

BIG BROTHER – SERIES 9

921.	Rachel Rice
922.	Maysoon
923.	93
924.	Nicole
925.	Darnell
926.	Because of a bomb scare
927.	Michael
928.	Mario and Lisa
929.	She was a PA
930.	44

SCOTTISH REALITY TV CONTESTANTS

931.	Kerry McGregor

932. *Big Brother: Celebrity Hijack*

933. *Lynne Moncrieff*

934. *Karly Ashworth*

935. *The Apprentice*

936. *Ayr*

937. *Federico Martone*

938. *Jason Cowan*

939. *44*

940. *The Apprentice: You're Fired!*

THE X FACTOR – 2009

941. *August*

942. *John and Edward, Kandy Rain and Miss Frank*

943. *True*

944. *Michael Bublé, Robbie Williams and George Michael*

945. *Will Young*

946. *John and Edward Grimes*

947. *Jamie Archer*

948. *Joe McElderry*

949. *True*

950. *Stacey Solomon*

DAVINA McCALL

951. *1967*

952. *True*

953. *Streetmate*

954. *True*

955. *Don't Try This At Home*

956. *Lucy Pascale*

957. *David Tennant*

958. *Matthew Robertson*

959. *A bikini*

960.   True (born in 2001, 2003 and 2006)

AMERCIA'S NEXT TOP MODEL

961.   Tyra Banks

962.   Teyona Anderson

963.   Paris

964.   Janice Dickinson

965.   UPN

966.   12

967.   Chantal Jones

968.   Nolé Marin

969.   Nicole Linkletter

970.   Barcelona

KATE LAWLER

971.   Louise

972.   Series 3

973.   She was the first female winner of Big Brother

974.   RI:SE

975.   Arsenal

976.   She ran the London Marathon

977.   Love Island

978.   Jonny

979.   22

980.   Spencer

BIG BROTHER – SERIES 10

981.   22

982.   Lisa Wallace

983.   Dogface

984.   Siavash

985.   Marcus Bentley

986. 93 days

987. *Stavros Flatley*

988. *Noirin*

989. *Freddie Fisher*

990. *44*

MICHELLE DEWBERRY

991. *Hull*

992. *St John Ambulance*

993. *Celebrity Scissorhands*

994. *Ruth Badger*

995. *False: Michelle was the winner of the second series*

996. *Silent Assassin, Steel Pixie and Ice Queen*

997. *The NSPCC*

998. *Anything is Possible*

999. *One year*

1000. *Because of a series of personal problems*

NOTES:

NOTES:

NOTES:

NOTES:

NOTES:

NOTES:

NOTES:

OTHER BOOKS BY CHRIS COWLIN:

* Celebrities' Favourite Football Teams

* The British TV Sitcom Quiz Book

* The Cricket Quiz Book

* The Gooners Quiz Book

* The Horror Film Quiz Book

* The Official Aston Villa Quiz Book

* The Official Birmingham City Quiz Book

* The Official Brentford Quiz Book

* The Official Bristol Rovers Quiz Book

* The Official Burnley Quiz Book

* The Official Bury Quiz Book

* The Official Carlisle United Quiz Book

* The Official Carry On Quiz Book

* The Official Chesterfield Football Club Quiz Book

* The Official Colchester United Quiz Book

* The Official Coventry City Quiz Book

* The Official Doncaster Rovers Quiz Book

* The Official Greenock Morton Quiz Book

* The Official Heart of Midlothian Quiz Book

* The Official Hereford United Quiz Book

* The Official Hull City Quiz Book

* The Official Ipswich Town Quiz Book

OTHER BOOKS BY CHRIS COWLIN:

* The Official Leicester City Quiz Book

* The Official Macclesfield Town Quiz Book

* The Official Norwich City Football Club Quiz

* The Official Notts County Quiz Book

* The Official Peterborough United Quiz Book

* The Official Port Vale Quiz Book

* The Official Queen of the South Quiz Book

* The Official Rochdale AFC Quiz Book

* The Official Rotherham United Quiz Book

* The Official Sheffield United Quiz Book

* The Official Shrewsbury Town Quiz Book

* The Official Stockport County Quiz Book

* The Official Walsall Football Club Quiz Book

* The Official Watford Football Club Quiz Book

* The Official West Bromwich Albion Quiz Book

* The Official Wolves Quiz Book

* The Official Yeovil Town Quiz Book

* The Reality Television Quiz Book

* The Southend United Quiz Book

* The Sunderland AFC Quiz Book

* The Ultimate Derby County Quiz Book

* The West Ham United Quiz Book

www.apexpublishing.co.uk